ChemLab

CARBON
CHEMISTRY

✦ Atlantic Europe Publishing

First published in 1998 by Atlantic Europe Publishing Company Limited, Greys Court Farm, Greys Court, Henley-on-Thames, Oxon, RG9 4PG, UK.

Author
Brian Knapp, BSc, PhD
Project consultant
Keith B. Walshaw, MA, BSc, DPhil
(Head of Chemistry, Leighton Park School)
Project Director
Duncan McCrae, BSc
Editor
Mary Sanders, BSc
Special photography
Ian Gledhill
Illustrations
David Woodroffe
The Ascenders Partnership
Designed and produced by
EARTHSCAPE EDITIONS
Print consultants
Chromo Litho Ltd
Reproduced in Malaysia by
Global Colour
Printed and bound in Italy by
L.E.G.O. SpA

Suggested cataloguing location
Knapp, Brian
    Carbon Chemistry
    ISBN 1 869860 62 4
    – ChemLab series, volume 9
540

Picture credits
All photographs are from the **Earthscape Editions** photolibrary except the following:
(c=centre t=top b=bottom l=left r=right)
ICI (UK) 24tr, **Mary Evans Picture Library** 6tr, 19tl, 20tc

This product is manufactured from sustainable managed forests. For every tree cut down at least one more is planted.

Contents

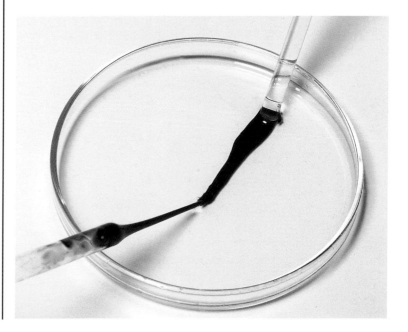

HOW TO USE THIS BOOK

These two pages show you how to get the most from this book.

❶ THE CONTENTS

Use the table of contents to see how this book is divided into themes. Each theme may have one or more demonstrations.

❷ THEMES

Each theme begins with a theory section on yellow-coloured paper. Major themes may contain several pages of theory for the demonstrations that are presented on the subsequent pages. They also contain biographies of scientists, whose work was important in the understanding of the theme.

❸ DEMONSTRATIONS

Demonstrations are at the heart of any chemistry study. However, many demonstrations cannot easily be shown to a whole class for health and safety reasons, because the demonstration requires a close-up view, because it is over too quickly, takes too long to complete, or because it requires special apparatus. The demonstrations shown here have been photographed especially to overcome these problems and give you a very close-up view of the key stages in each reaction.

The text, pictures and diagrams are closely connected. To get the best from the demonstration, look closely at each picture as soon as its reference occurs in the text.

Many of the pictures show enlarged views of parts of the demonstration to help you see exactly what is happening. Notice, too, that most pictures form part of a sequence. You will find that it pays to look at the picture sequence more than once, and always be careful to make sure you can see exactly what is described in any picture before you move on.

The main heading for a demonstration or a set of demonstrations.

An introduction expands on the heading, summarising the demonstration or group of demonstrations and their context in the theme.

Each demonstration is carefully explained and illustrated with photographs and, where necessary, with diagrams, tables and graphs. The illustrations referred to are numbered ①, ②, ③, etc.

Chemical equations are shown where appropriate (see the explanation of equations at the bottom of page 5).

The photographs show the key stages that you might see if you witness a demonstration at first-hand. Examine them very carefully against the text description.

APPARATUS

The demonstrations have been carefully conducted as representative examples of the main chemical processes. The apparatus used is standard, but other choices are possible and you may see different equipment in your laboratory, so make sure you understand the principles behind the apparatus selected. The key pieces of apparatus are defined in the glossary.

❹ GLOSSARY OF TECHNICAL TERMS

Words with which you may be unfamiliar are shown in small capitals where they first occur in the text. Use the glossary on pages 66–74 to find more information about these technical words. Over 400 items are presented alphabetically.

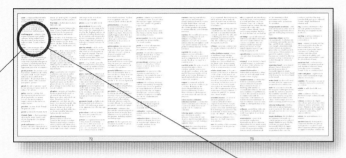

oxidising agent: a substance that removes electrons from another substance being oxidised (and therefore is itself reduced) in a redox reaction. *Example:* chlorine (Cl₂).

❺ INDEX TO ALL VOLUMES IN THE SET

To look for key words in any of the 12 volumes that make up the ChemLab set, use the Master Index on pages 75 to 80. The instructions on page 75 show you how to cross-reference between volumes.

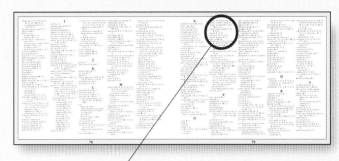

The most important locations of the term 'oxidising agent' are given in a master index which includes references to all of the volumes in the ChemLab set.

ABBREVIATIONS

Units are in the international metric system. Some units of measurement are abbreviated, or shortened, as follows:

°C = degrees Celsius
km = kilometre
m = metre
cm = centimetre
mm = millimetre
sq m = square metre
g = gram
kg = kilogram
kJ = kilojoule
l = litre

❻ CHEMICAL EQUATIONS

Important or relevant chemical equations are shown in written and symbolic form together with additional information.

What the reaction equation illustrates

Where relevant, the oxidation state is shown as Roman numerals in brackets.

Word equation

EQUATION: Reaction of copper and nitric acid
Copper + nitric acid ⇨ copper(II) nitrate + water + nitrogen dioxide

Symbol equation
The symbols for each element can be found in any Periodic Table.

$Cu(s) + 4HNO_3(conc) ⇨ Cu(NO_3)_2(aq) + 2H_2O(l) + 2NO_2(g)$
Blue

The symbol indicating the state of each substance is shown as follows:
(*s*) = solid
(*g*) = gaseous
(*l*) = liquid
(*aq*) = aqueous
(*conc*) = concentrated

The two halves of the chemical equation are separated by the arrow that shows the progression of the reaction. Each side of the equation must balance.

Sometimes additional descriptions are given below the symbol equation.

The correct number of atoms, ions and molecules and their proportions in any compound are shown by the numbers. A free electron is shown as an e⁻.

INTRODUCTION

Nine-tenths of all substances contain carbon, usually in a complex COMPOUND involving hydrogen. However, in a few cases, such as with the gases, carbon monoxide and carbon dioxide, carbon is not connected with hydrogen. These simpler compounds were the easiest and the first examples of carbon-based substances to be investigated, and they make up the demonstrations in the first part of this book.

The first scientific analysis of natural materials began by using COMBUSTION. For example, the French chemist Antoine Lavoisier, who was interested in the newly discovered gas oxygen, believed that oxides such as carbon dioxide are formed during combustion of all materials.

Because burning organic matter (substances that are connected in some way with plant and animal materials) in air always produced carbon dioxide (CO_2) and water (H_2O), Lavoisier deduced that all organic material must contain carbon and hydrogen (the oxygen coming from the air). Thus began the study of the vast field known as ORGANIC CHEMISTRY. Demonstrations involving organic substances make up the second part of this book.

The adsorption properties of activated charcoal

ACTIVATED CHARCOAL is carbon that has a very large reactive surface area (about 2000 sq m of surface area for every gram in weight of charcoal). It is able to ADSORB large numbers of gas molecules on this vast surface. This impressive property means that activated charcoal has been widely used as a gas filter.

Demonstration: adsorption of bromine vapour using activated charcoal

The apparatus consists of a gas jar containing brown bromine vapour and some activated charcoal pieces. Because bromine is poisonous, the demonstration is performed in a fume chamber.

Pieces of activated charcoal are dropped into a gas jar containing bromine vapour and the cover glass replaced (①).

Within a minute, the colour of the gas becomes noticeably lighter as fewer free bromine molecules remain in the jar (②).

Within five minutes, the gas jar is colourless, because all of the bromine molecules are now adsorbed on to the surface of the activated charcoal, with none remaining as free gas (③).

Remarks

Once all the sites on the activated charcoal have been used, it has to be thrown away. It cannot be reactivated. Although activated charcoal works well for many hydrocarbons, chlorine and similar gases, carbon will not adsorb oxygen or nitrogen.

① ② ③

Glass cover slip seals gas jar

Bromine vapour

Activated charcoal

Combustion of carbon and its oxides

Carbon monoxide and carbon dioxide are oxides of carbon. Carbon and carbon monoxide can both be OXIDISED, and so they combust. Carbon dioxide is the fully oxidised state of carbon. This is the reason why carbon dioxide will not combust.

Demonstration 1: combustion of carbon in a stream of oxygen

Carbon combusts in air (which contains about one-fifth oxygen by volume) to give off carbon dioxide. It does not give off any combustible vapours and therefore does not produce flames.

Carbon combusts more rapidly in pure oxygen because of the increased number of oxygen molecules available to take part in the reaction.

In this demonstration, a stick of charcoal (carbon) is placed in the end of a glass tube and is heated with a Bunsen flame until it glows white-hot (①). The flame is then removed and the charcoal colour changes to a red glow.

The tube is now connected to an oxygen supply. As the oxygen passes over the charcoal, it immediately glows white-hot and releases many INCANDESCENT particles into the laboratory and back up the glass tube (②).

EQUATION: Combustion of carbon
Carbon + oxygen ⇨ carbon dioxide
$C(s) + O_2(g) \Rightarrow CO_2(g)$

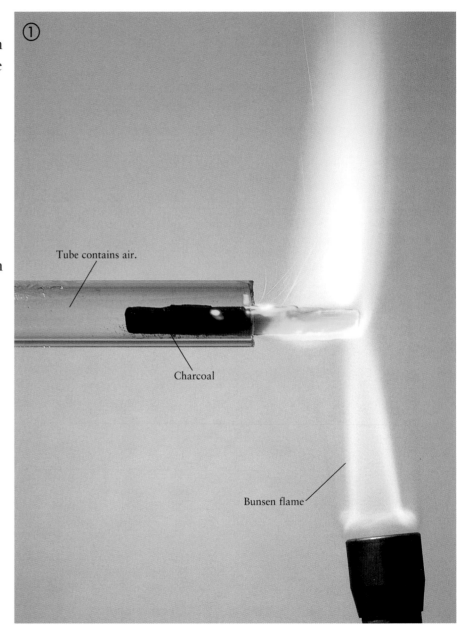

①

Tube contains air.

Charcoal

Bunsen flame

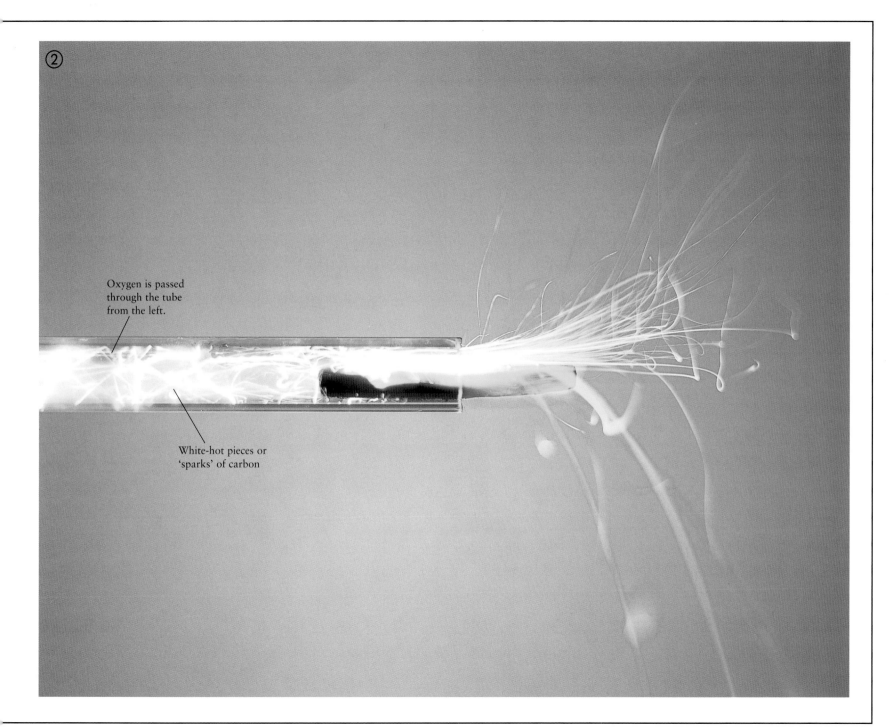

②

Oxygen is passed
through the tube
from the left.

White-hot pieces or
'sparks' of carbon

9

Demonstration 2: combustion of carbon in a gas jar of oxygen

EQUATION: Combustion of carbon in oxygen
Carbon + oxygen ⇨ carbon dioxide
$C(s) + O_2(g) \rightarrow CO_2(g)$

In this demonstration, a piece of charcoal is held with tongs in a Bunsen flame. When the carbon is heated in air with a Bunsen flame, it glows, indicating that combustion is taking place (③). However, when the hot charcoal is placed in a gas jar containing oxygen, the charcoal combusts more strongly, and a ball of white-hot carbon is produced (④). Notice, however, that despite the spectacular nature of the combustion, no flames are produced because there is only one gas involved. Carbon dioxide is given off until the oxygen is used up.

Gas jar filled with oxygen   Bunsen burner

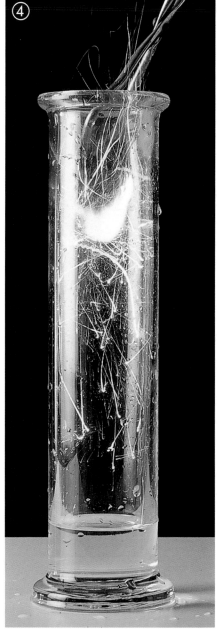

Demonstration 3: combustion of carbon monoxide

When a lighted splint is introduced into a gas jar of carbon monoxide (⑤), a bright blue flame forms at the top and quickly runs down to the bottom until all the gas is used up.

The combustion of carbon monoxide produces a flame because two combustible gases, carbon monoxide and oxygen from the air, are mixing and reacting. The product is carbon dioxide gas.

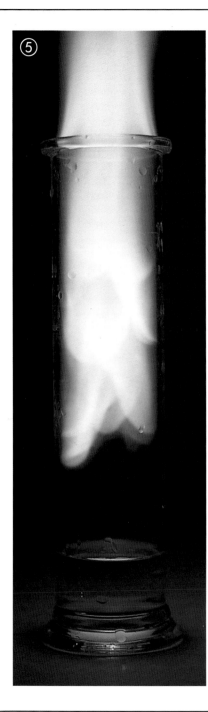

EQUATION: Combustion of carbon monoxide
Carbon monoxide + oxygen ➪ carbon dioxide
$$2CO(g) + O_2(g) ➪ 2CO_2(g)$$

Demonstration 4: attempted combustion of carbon dioxide gas

When a lighted splint is introduced into a gas jar containing carbon dioxide (⑥), it is rapidly extinguished (⑦).

Carbon dioxide cannot be oxidised further. As combustion is an OXIDATION process, if the gas cannot be oxidised, no combustion can occur and no flame can be sustained.

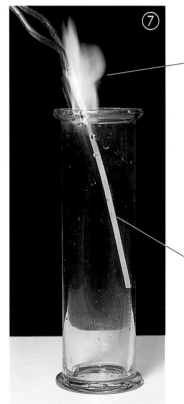

The splint remains lit in the air above the gas jar.

Carbon dioxide does not support combustion, and when a lighted splint is put into a gas jar containing the gas, the splint is extinguished.

11

Carbon as a reducing agent in the extraction of metals

Carbon can be used as a REDUCING AGENT to remove oxygen from metal oxides such as lead(II) oxide or copper(II) oxide.

Demonstration 1: reduction of lead oxide

A quantity of orange lead oxide (lead(II) oxide, PbO) powder is added to a similar quantity of powdered charcoal (①). The two substances are then mixed thoroughly before being placed in a crucible (②). The mixing is important because as much of the oxide as possible needs to be in intimate contact with the carbon reducing agent.

The lead oxide and carbon mixture is heated very strongly in the crucible using a Bunsen flame (③). The carbon reduces the oxide and forms a number of small lead globules (④), which can be worked into one large globule using a metal spatula (⑤). Colourless carbon monoxide gas is given off during this reaction. When the heat is removed, the molten globule cools to leave solid lead.

Remarks

Lead has a low melting point, so this demonstration proceeds under the heat of an ordinary Bunsen flame.

① Ground charcoal

Lead(II) oxide

②

Crucible and tray

Pipe-clay triangle

EQUATION: Reduction of lead monoxide
Lead(II) oxide + carbon ⇨ lead + carbon monoxide
$2PbO(s) + 2C(s) ⇨ 2Pb(s) + 2CO(g)$

Reducing carbon dioxide to carbon monoxide

Carbon monoxide gas can be prepared by passing carbon dioxide over white-hot carbon, which, in this situation, acts as a reducing agent.

Demonstration: reduction of carbon dioxide using white-hot charcoal

The central part of the apparatus used consists of a gas-fired laboratory furnace (①). This is essentially a ceramic frame, which has a hole passing through its centre. A silica tube can be placed in this hole. Gas jets play on the silica tube, thereby heating the tube and its contents. The ceramic frame stores the heat, thereby allowing temperatures in the furnace to rise sufficiently to make carbon white-hot.

Carbon granules are placed in the silica tube (②). The tube is then connected to a supply of carbon dioxide gas (in this case produced from a KIPP'S APPARATUS) and to a gas collecting system. Carbon monoxide is insoluble and so can be collected in a gas jar over water in a pneumatic trough.

Between the furnace and the gas jar is a DRESCHEL BOTTLE. This is a particular design of wash bottle consisting of an entry tube that reaches to the bottom of the bottle, and an exit tube near the top. Its function in this demonstration is to remove any unaltered carbon dioxide gas. Therefore, the Dreschel bottle is half-filled with sodium hydroxide solution. The carbon dioxide will react with the water in the solution to form carbonic acid. The carbonic acid will

then react in turn with the sodium hydroxide to form sodium carbonate in water. The carbon monoxide doesn't react with the sodium hydroxide and bubbles through unchanged.

The gas supply is lit and the furnace allowed to reach operating temperature, which may take half an hour (③, see page 16). The tap to the Kipp's apparatus is then turned on so that carbon dioxide gas can pass over the white-hot carbon and be reduced to carbon monoxide (④, ⑤ & ⑥, see page 17). When the

①

Kipp's apparatus is used to produce a steady supply of carbon dioxide.

Dilute hydrochloric acid is reacted with marble (calcium carbonate) chips to produce carbon dioxide gas.

gas jar is full, it can be removed from the apparatus and tested to verify that it contains carbon monoxide. A lighted splint placed inside the gas will immediately ignite with a blue flame (see page 10).

Remarks

During the demonstration, it is obvious that more bubbling occurs in the Dreschel bottle than in the gas jar. In other words, it appears that the gas is being lost as it goes through the Dreschel bottle, which is to be expected if some of it is carbon dioxide. However, the volume of gas passing through the Dreschel bottle cannot be compared easily with the volume of the bubbles rising in the

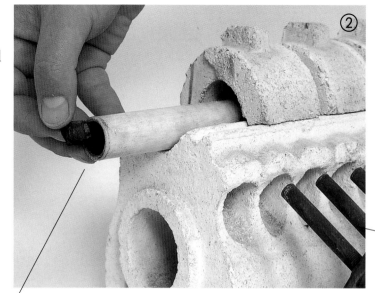

②

Gas jets will heat furnace.

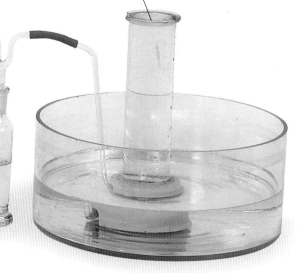

Apparatus for collecting a gas over water. This consists of a gas jar seated on a beehive shelf in a water-filled glass trough (pneumatic trough).

This furnace is heated by gas jets. Heat is conserved by surrounding the apparatus with a ceramic liner.

Pieces of carbon, in the form of charcoal, are placed inside a silica tube which, in turn, is connected to the Kipp's apparatus.

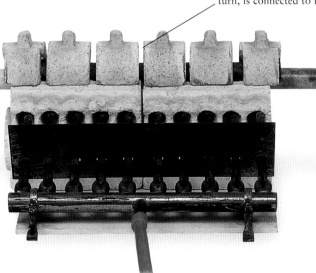

A Dreschel bottle is used for removing carbon dioxide gas by bubbling it through sodium hydroxide.

gas jar because the bubbles that rise in the gas jar are not necessarily the same size as the ones that bubble through the Dreschel bottle.

The volume of gas that can be produced by the Kipp's apparatus can be substantial, and therefore gas can accumulate in the gas jar very quickly. However, this may not all be carbon monoxide! The rate at which gas passes through the apparatus needs to be slowed down to ensure effective 'scrubbing' (removal of the carbon dioxide in the sodium hydroxide) in the Dreschel bottle. This is because it is only the outside of the bubble that interacts with the reagent and so small, slow-moving bubbles will be scrubbed more effectively than fast-moving, large bubbles.

Notice that carbon will reduce carbon dioxide to carbon monoxide at very high temperatures, whereas soot is formed in INCOMPLETE COMBUSTION at low temperatures.

③

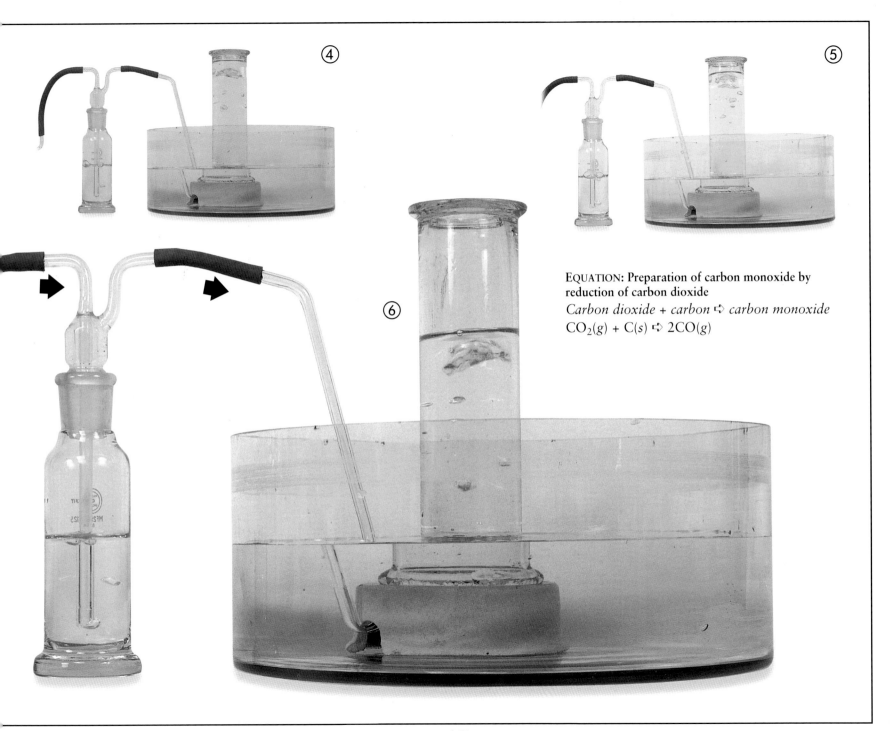

④

⑤

⑥

EQUATION: Preparation of carbon monoxide by reduction of carbon dioxide
Carbon dioxide + carbon ⇨ carbon monoxide
$CO_2(g) + C(s) ⇨ 2CO(g)$

ORGANIC COMPOUNDS

People have been using organic compounds since earliest times. For example, vinegar and alcohol (wine) are made by fermenting grapes, and dyes can be made from many natural plant juices. Soaps can be made by boiling fats with soda ash.

Yet, despite thousands of years of their use, carbon-based substances remained difficult to work with, and so carbon chemistry was little developed before the end of the 18th century.

Naturally, scientists wanted to understand how the compounds were formed so that they could synthesise (make) new ones. Scientists expected the enormous variety of substances they saw in nature to be formed from an equally bewildering range of elements. Yet, for most of the substances they analysed, it was found that they contained just the same few elements: carbon, hydrogen and oxygen, sometimes accompanied by nitrogen, sulphur, phosphorus and the halogens (chlorine, etc.).

In fact, the origin of most organic material is very simple. It is produced when plants transform carbon dioxide and water during PHOTOSYNTHESIS (①).

EQUATION: Photosynthesis
① *Carbon dioxide + water ⇨ sugar + oxygen*
$6CO_2(g) + 6H_2O(l) ⇨ C_6H_{12}O_6(s) + 6O_2(g)$
Sunlight

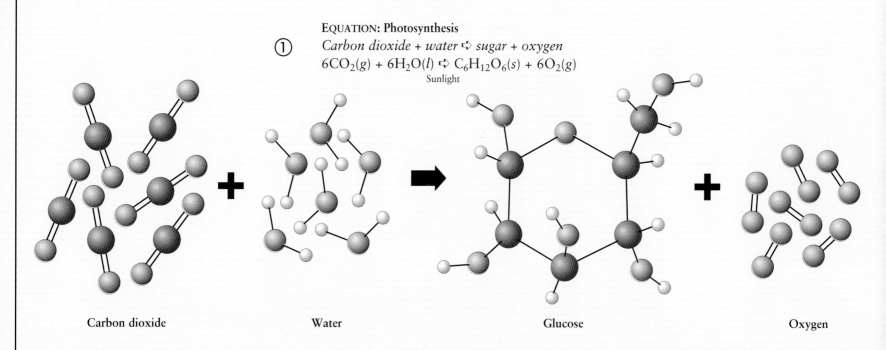

Carbon dioxide   Water   Glucose   Oxygen

Justus von Liebig

Justus von Liebig (1803–1873) was a German chemist, famous for developing a special form of condenser, but whose real legacy to chemistry was in the field of organic chemistry. His father sold dyes and drugs, and at that time it was common for such people also to experiment with making new substances.

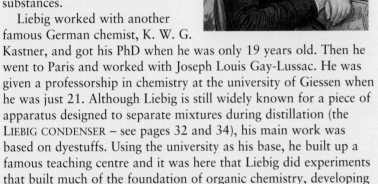

Liebig worked with another famous German chemist, K. W. G. Kastner, and got his PhD when he was only 19 years old. Then he went to Paris and worked with Joseph Louis Gay-Lussac. He was given a professorship in chemistry at the university of Giessen when he was just 21. Although Liebig is still widely known for a piece of apparatus designed to separate mixtures during distillation (the LIEBIG CONDENSER – see pages 32 and 34), his main work was based on dyestuffs. Using the university as his base, he built up a famous teaching centre and it was here that Liebig did experiments that built much of the foundation of organic chemistry, developing new ways of analysing complex organic compounds.

Identifying the elements in organic substances

As more investigations were undertaken, scientists were forced to the conclusion that many different substances must have similar properties. For example, it was discovered that the starch of plants reacts with sulphuric acid to yield (among other substances) glucose, an important sugar. It was also found that sulphuric acid had the same effect on linen rags. The term CARBOHYDRATE (in other words, hydrated carbon) was coined for those substances that contained carbon and also the same proportion of atoms of hydrogen to oxygen as is found in water. (Demonstrations with carbohydrates will be found on pages 52 to 55.)

It was important to be able to measure the elements in organic compounds accurately. This was first achieved by Justus von Liebig of Germany in 1830. A sample of an organic substance was burned in a glass combustion tube containing copper oxide as an oxidising agent. The water that formed was collected in a weighed drying tube and the carbon dioxide in a weighed bulb containing potassium hydroxide. The weights of hydrogen and carbon in the sample could then be calculated from the weights of water and carbon dioxide produced from the combusted sample. This principle is shown in the demonstration on page 26.

Liebig was also able to find a way to isolate nitrogen separately from carbon–hydrogen. An even better procedure for finding nitrogen was later introduced by Alexander Dumas. He burned the sample in a combustion tube containing copper oxide in an atmosphere of carbon dioxide; nitrogen gas was then collected in a tube over a concentrated solution of potassium hydroxide, which absorbed the water and carbon dioxide formed during the combustion. In this way the percentage of nitrogen in the sample could be found.

For example, when benzene is analysed in this way, the oxides obtained are water (H_2O) and carbon dioxide (CO_2). Liebig's procedure suggests that

Carl Wilhelm Scheele

Carl Wilhelm Scheele (1742–1786) was born in a part of Sweden that is now Germany, and was apprenticed to an apothecary. He never earned a university degree and remained a pharmacist throughout his life. At this time it was typical for pharmacists to prepare their own medicines and do research into them as well.

Because he did not move in the company of those working in universities, he was not aware of other advances that were being made, and so he did not work on any particular range of subjects, nor did he see the need to make his discoveries known quickly. Thus, he performed many experiments on an almost random array of subjects depending on what materials he could get hold of. But the result of his enormous enthusiasm and talent was that he discovered a wider range of substances than anyone else.

Many of the gases Scheele discovered were discovered independently a little later by others and credited to them. The most famous of these is oxygen, credited to Joseph Priestley, but discovered by Scheele three years earlier.

Scheele isolated a wide range of organic substances, including tartaric acid, citric acid, and oxalic acid. He also discovered hydrogen sulphide, hydrogen fluoride, and hydrogen cyanide. He either discovered or greatly contributed to the discovery of manganese, nitrogen, oxygen, tungsten, barium, molybdenum, and chlorine. He called oxygen 'fire air' and nitrogen 'foul air' because it did not support combustion. He also discovered that light alters the colour of silver salts (a discovery that ultimately led to the invention of the photographic film).

benzene should have a formula that contains only carbon and hydrogen in equal amounts and so would be CH. The 'MOLECULAR WEIGHT' of benzene by this method would be 13. But other laboratory experiments show that benzene's molecular weight is 78, which is six times greater than 13. So, the molecular formula of benzene must be C_6H_6.

Separating natural mixtures

Because natural substances are mixtures of compounds, much early attention was given to their separation (see page 32 for SIMPLE DISTILLATION). Michel Eugène Chevreul, a French chemist, working in the early 19th century, was the first person to isolate a range of substances from natural mixtures by using INERT SOLVENTS, and by using the fact that each substance had a unique melting and boiling point. In time, this led to the important laboratory technique called FRACTIONAL DISTILLATION (see page 34).

The organic mixture most widely used by the chemical industry today is petroleum. The word petroleum comes from the Latin words 'petra' and 'oleum', meaning 'rock' and 'oil', respectively. Petroleum is therefore a 'catch-all' name for a wide range of gases, liquids and some solids, which form in the rocks of the Earth's crust.

Classifying organic substances

The majority of substances in the world are organic compounds. There are many groups of organic compounds, classified by their structures, which are explained on the following pages.

(a) hydrocarbons

Hydrocarbons form a large group of simple organic substances that contain *only* carbon and hydrogen atoms. This group contains such important substances as methane (natural gas) and petrol.

Carbon atoms always form four chemical BONDS, that is, they can each bond to four other atoms. In inorganic chemistry, many compounds form which are linked by single BONDS between atoms. All hydrocarbons in which the carbon atoms are joined

(Right) This represents a molecule of the simplest hydrocarbon, methane (CH_4).·

These three molecules are all alkanes. They are all saturated hydrocarbons because they have only single bonds (see page 2).

(Above) This represents a molecule of the hydrocarbon ethane (C_2H_6).

(Above) This represents a molecule of propane (C_3H_8).

by a single bond have a name which ends in **–ane**, such as ethane, methane and butane. Demonstrations involving methane are shown on pages 25 to 29.

However, organic compounds do not always follow this single-bond rule. It was discovered that, in some compounds, the carbon atoms shared two bonds (known as double bonds) or three bonds (triple bonds), giving these compounds special properties. Hydrocarbons in which the carbon atoms are joined by double bonds have a name which ends in **–ene**, such as ethene, while those with triple bonds have names that end in **–yne**, such as ethyne. Demonstrations involving these hydrocarbons are given on pages 36 to 39.

CLASSIFYING HYDROCARBONS BY STRUCTURE

Chemists classify hydrocarbons by the structure of their molecules: that is, whether they consist of long branched chains, or rings, and whether the chains or rings have single, double or triple bonds. The most reactive are those with triple bonds, while the (relatively) least reactive are the saturated hydrocarbons with only single bonds (see page 22).

The hydrocarbons that form chain structures are known as ALKANES, and include the gases methane, butane and the liquid octane. ALKENES contain more reactive double bonds and include substances such as ethene and propene. The ALKYNES have even more reactive triple bonds and include substances such as ethyne (acetylene).

The hydrocarbons that contain types of rings are called AROMATIC HYDROCARBONS. They received their name from the fact that the first members of the group to be identified had a strong scent. Naphthalene is an important example. Hydrogen atoms on the rings can be substituted by other groups to make a wide range of new substances.

21

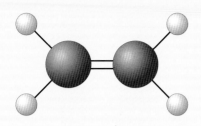

(Left) This represents a molecule of the hydrocarbon ethene (C_2H_4). It is an unsaturated hydrocarbon because it has a double bond. Alkenes such as ethene are characterised by double bonds.

(Right) This represents a molecule of the hydrocarbon ethyne (C_2H_2). It is an unsaturated hydrocarbon because it has a triple bond. Alkynes such as ethyne are characterised by triple bonds.

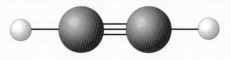

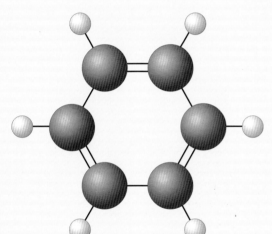

(Left) This represents a molecule of the hydrocarbon benzene (C_6H_6). It is an unsaturated hydrocarbon because it has double bonds.

SATURATED AND UNSATURATED HYDROCARBONS

A key difference between one hydrocarbon and another is whether or not the hydrocarbon molecule contains the maximum possible number of hydrogen atoms, and whether its carbon atoms are bonded together by single bonds consisting of a single pair of electrons.

If a substance has the maximum possible number of hydrogen atoms, and the carbon atoms are all single bonded, no more hydrogen atoms can be attached. This substance is known as a SATURATED HYDROCARBON.

However, in cases in which carbon atoms have double and triple bonds, they share two or three pairs of electrons between them, even though only one pair of electrons is needed to bond the carbons together. This means that the second and third pair represent bonds that can be broken, and to which more hydrogen atoms can be attached. These are therefore known as UNSATURATED HYDROCARBONS. Hydrogen atoms can be added to unsaturated compounds to form saturated compounds. They can also react with bromine, chlorine, and many other reagents, forming a whole new range of substances.

Saturated and unsaturated compounds are common in nature. Oils are unsaturated fats, whereas solid fats are made with saturated molecules. Both are compounds called 'esters' and contain oxygen.

It is possible to convert oils to fats by adding hydrogen and so saturating the oil molecules. This allows, for example, vegetable oils to be used in making margarines and spreads.

(b) alcohols

One of the most important hydrocarbons is the gas ethene. If steam is added to it, the double bond of the ethene will open up, hydrogen and oxygen will be added to the structure, and the result is the liquid ethanol, more commonly called alcohol.

The alcohols are a large group of natural organic substances, which all contain C and OH in their structure (as compared with hydrocarbons that simply have C and H in their structure). Thus methanol (a poisonous alcohol) has the formula CH_3OH and ethanol (the main intoxicating substance in alcoholic drinks) has the formula C_2H_5OH. Alcohols also include ethane-1,2-diol (otherwise known as ethylene glycol or antifreeze) and propane-1,2,3-triol (glycerine or glycerol).

Many alcohols readily mix with water and make excellent solvents for organic compounds.

Alcohols can be prepared by heating or fermenting naturally occurring vegetable products. Thus ethanol is obtained from wheat, maize and other grains, while methanol was traditionally prepared entirely by the DESTRUCTIVE DISTILLATION (PYROLYSIS) of hard woods. The wood, heated in an airless container, produces a mixture of organic substances that are then separated by fractional distillation. This is the historic reason why some people still refer to ethanol as 'grain alcohol' and methanol as 'wood alcohol'. Demonstrations of these methods of separation are shown on pages 34 and 40.

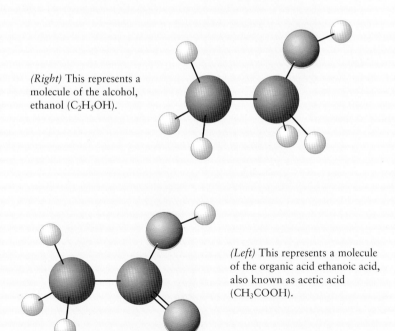

(Right) This represents a molecule of the alcohol, ethanol (C_2H_5OH).

(Left) This represents a molecule of the organic acid ethanoic acid, also known as acetic acid (CH_3COOH).

Fuels

Many people associate organic materials, and especially hydrocarbons, with fuels. In fact, a very wide variety of substances (both inorganic and organic) can be used as fuels. Nevertheless, the majority of the fuels used (for example, as motor car fuel) are hydrocarbons. Simple hydrocarbons such as methane and butane are burned as natural gases. Most natural materials – wood, coal, petroleum and so on – actually contain a variety of substances. That is why, to obtain the hydrocarbons, alcohols and other substances from these mixtures, the various fractions have to be separated out, usually by means of heat. Alcohol-based fuels are demonstrated on page 50.

Synthesising substances

As scientists grew more familiar with natural substances, they began to find ways in which they could not only separate them, but also make, or synthesise, them from combinations of the elements. For example, as early as 1862, the Frenchman, Pierre Eugène Marcelin Berthelot, prepared acetylene (ethyne) by passing hydrogen through an electric arc formed between carbon rods.

From here, it was a straightforward step to begin to synthesise compounds based on carbon and hydrogen that were not found in nature. The raw material for much of this work was coal. Today, it is based largely on petroleum. Some of the materials that are synthesised are discussed under the section on polymers beginning on page 56.

INDUSTRIAL PROCESSING OF PETROLEUM

Industrial processes use heat to distil or CRACK complex organic mixtures or compounds in a continuous, highly automated process. The two main processes of cracking and distilling can be combined. For example, crude oil is heated in towers so that the lighter parts of the mixture vaporise. The separate fractions can be obtained by making use of the various boiling points of the substances in the mixture.

A simple process of boiling separates only about one-tenth of the crude oil. The remainder has to be processed again, by cracking, so that the large, heavy hydrocarbon molecules (which are required by industry in much smaller quantities than the lighter, smaller molecules) are broken up into smaller ones. A combination of heat and pressure is used. In this way, the products of the refinery can be tailored to market needs.

(*Left*) This is a cracking unit in a petrochemical plant. The slim towers are fractionating columns.

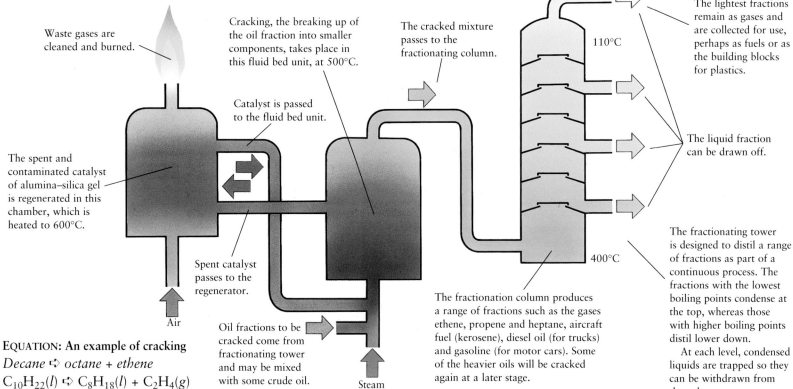

Waste gases are cleaned and burned.

Cracking, the breaking up of the oil fraction into smaller components, takes place in this fluid bed unit, at 500°C.

The cracked mixture passes to the fractionating column.

The lightest fractions remain as gases and are collected for use, perhaps as fuels or as the building blocks for plastics.

110°C

Catalyst is passed to the fluid bed unit.

The spent and contaminated catalyst of alumina–silica gel is regenerated in this chamber, which is heated to 600°C.

The liquid fraction can be drawn off.

Spent catalyst passes to the regenerator.

Air

400°C

The fractionating tower is designed to distil a range of fractions as part of a continuous process. The fractions with the lowest boiling points condense at the top, whereas those with higher boiling points distil lower down.

At each level, condensed liquids are trapped so they can be withdrawn from the column.

The fractionation column produces a range of fractions such as the gases ethene, propene and heptane, aircraft fuel (kerosene), diesel oil (for trucks) and gasoline (for motor cars). Some of the heavier oils will be cracked again at a later stage.

Oil fractions to be cracked come from fractionating tower and may be mixed with some crude oil.

Steam

EQUATION: An example of cracking
Decane ⇨ octane + ethene
$C_{10}H_{22}(l) \Rightarrow C_8H_{18}(l) + C_2H_4(g)$

Combustion of methane

Natural gas, which is the usual mains gas supply to laboratories, is mainly methane (CH_4), the simplest of the hydrocarbons (substances containing only carbon and hydrogen atoms).

Demonstration 1: burning methane in a Bunsen burner

A Bunsen burner enables natural gas to be combusted in a controlled way. The Bunsen burner consists of a base through which the gas enters, a vertical pipe which has a hole in the side near the base, and a collar which can be rotated to cover or uncover the hole in the pipe.

When the gas tap is turned on and gas flows up the pipe, it produces a draught that can suck air in through the hole near the base. The collar around the pipe enables the amount of oxygen mixing with the methane to be controlled.

Collar controls air intake.

(a) yellow flame

When the air hole is closed, oxygen cannot enter the pipe, and natural gas and oxygen can only mix at the top of the pipe. The mixing is a DIFFUSION process and a smoky yellow flame is formed, which is similar to that of a candle burning (①).

The majority of the flame is luminous yellow because incomplete combustion occurs, and although all of the hydrogen is converted to steam, and most carbon is converted to carbon dioxide, some carbon remains as soot particles, which then begin to glow (incandesce).

(b) blue flame

When the air hole is open, air can enter the Burner at the base of the pipe and mix with the natural gas before it reaches the top. As a result, complete combustion occurs above the pipe, and a blue, soot-free flame is produced (②). Without soot there can be no yellow incandescence.

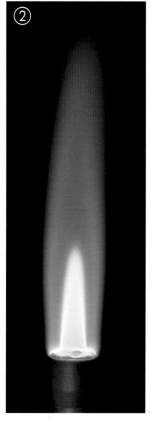

Remarks

The occasional yellow flicker occurs when particles of dust floating in the air get pulled into the Bunsen flame.

EQUATION: Combustion of methane
Methane + oxygen ⇨ carbon dioxide + water vapour
$CH_4(g) + 2O_2(g) \Rightarrow CO_2(g) + 2H_2O(g)$

Demonstration 2: methane contains hydrogen

This demonstration shows that hydrocarbons contain hydrogen (shown here as a component of water) and carbon (shown here as a component of carbon dioxide).

The source of the hydrocarbon is natural gas, which is mainly methane. The apparatus is designed to detect water and carbon dioxide gas (①).

When a gaseous hydrocarbon, such as methane or butane is burned, well mixed with air, all of the products will be gases. No solid particles of soot are formed from these simple hydrocarbons. In this demonstration, therefore, the gas will be burned below an inverted funnel so that the products of combustion are carried with the hot air into an upturned funnel and from there to the detecting equipment (②).

Although the hot air will carry the gases into the funnel (③, see page 28), this is not sufficient to make sure they pass through the system. The whole apparatus is therefore connected to a water-driven suction pump, which pulls air and combustion gases through the system (④).

The first test is for water, using anhydrous copper(II) sulphate (⑤, see page 29). This white powder turns blue as it absorbs water (⑥). Notice that a side-arm boiling tube is used to contain the copper sulphate, and that the entry tube reaches to the base of the boiling tube, so that all gases pass close to the

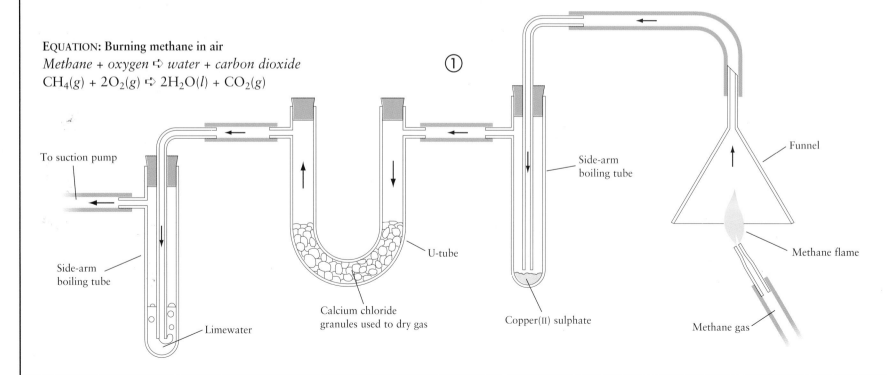

EQUATION: Burning methane in air
Methane + oxygen ⇨ water + carbon dioxide
$CH_4(g) + 2O_2(g) \Rightarrow 2H_2O(l) + CO_2(g)$

①

To suction pump

Side-arm boiling tube

Limewater

Calcium chloride granules used to dry gas

U-tube

Side-arm boiling tube

Copper(II) sulphate

Funnel

Methane flame

Methane gas

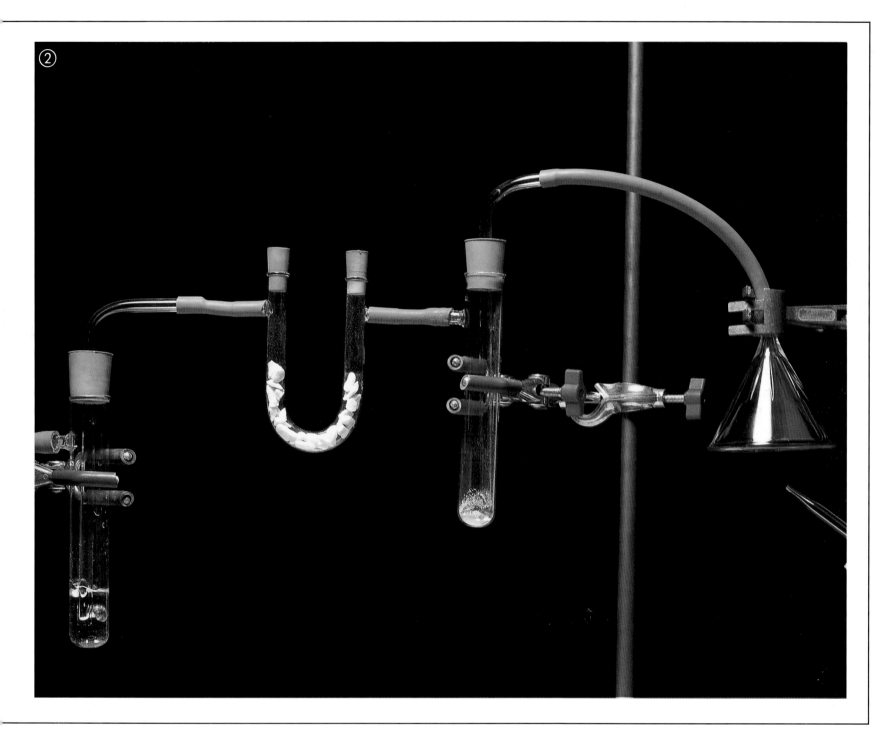

copper(II) sulphate before exiting from the side arm.

To ensure that no water vapour returns from the next stage of the apparatus, the gas leaving the water-testing tube is passed over anhydrous calcium chloride in a U-tube. This removes all water vapour and so only dry gases can pass. Thus it prevents any moist air from the limewater in the second tube getting back into the tube containing the copper(II) sulphate if the suction pump does not maintain an adequate flow.

The second side-arm boiling tube contains calcium hydroxide solution (limewater, ⑦). If the combustion gases contain carbon dioxide, the reaction of the calcium hydroxide and the limewater will make calcium carbonate precipitate as a fine suspension and the limewater will appear cloudy (⑧). The side arm of the limewater tube is connected to the suction pump.

It is important to verify that the changes observed only occur as a result of combustion, so the suction pump is switched on, and air allowed to flow through the detecting system for a few minutes before the flame is lit. The fact that the copper(II) sulphate

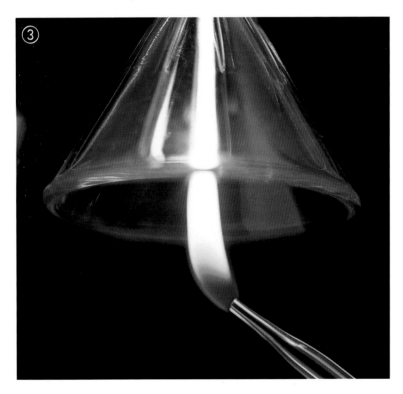

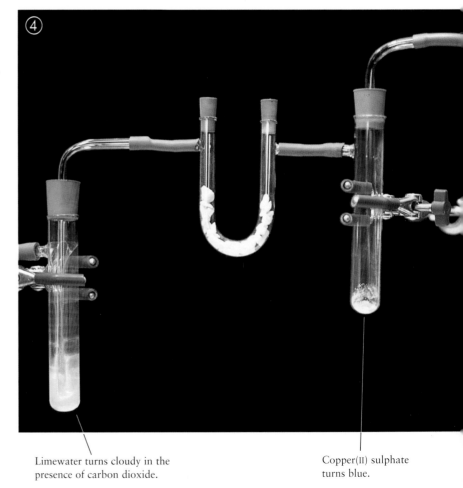

Limewater turns cloudy in the presence of carbon dioxide.

Copper(II) sulphate turns blue.

remains white, and the limewater remains clear, shows that the air passing through the apparatus is not, itself, responsible for any changes.

Within a few seconds of lighting the gas, the limewater turns cloudy, showing the presence of carbon dioxide gas, and therefore that carbon present in the natural gas has combined with oxygen from the air.

The change in the copper(II) sulphate (which shows that water is a product from the reaction, and therefore hydrogen is contained in the natural gas) takes several minutes.

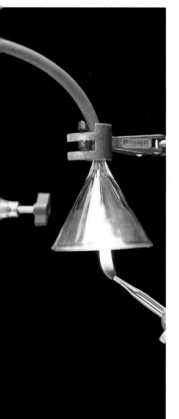

The speed of reaction of the copper(II) sulphate depends on the amount of material in the tube. It is tempting to put a large amount of copper(II) sulphate in the tube, but this will require a large amount of water vapour to make it change colour, so the rule is, the smaller the amount of copper(II) sulphate in the tube, the faster the material will turn blue.

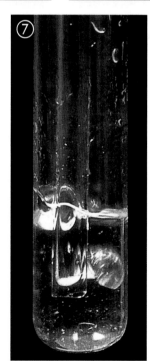

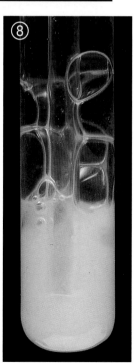

EQUATION: Combustion of methane
Methane + oxygen ⇨ carbon dioxide + water vapour
$CH_4(g) + 2O_2(g) ⇨ CO_2(g) + 2H_2O(g)$

Oxidation of an alcohol

Alcohols are readily oxidised. This might be done, for example, as a first step in making nylon (see page 57). The energy difference between the reactants and the products is readily seen as the oxidation occurs. This demonstration is a clear example of how a reaction can be used for very different purposes – as a source of energy or a source of chemical products.

Demonstration: oxidation of cyclohexanol

This demonstration uses the alcohol, cyclohexanol, and the oxidising agent, nitric acid. The result is to change the cyclohexanol into adipic (hexandioic) acid, one of the starting materials that can be used in the preparation of nylon.

The apparatus consists of a large empty gas jar with stirring thermometer, a small volume of (colourless) cyclohexanol in one measuring cylinder and a small volume of (colourless) nitric acid in the other (①). It is important to notice that there is a small volume of starting reactants being used here; large quantities can be dangerous. The reaction is performed in a fume chamber. The thermometer will give an indication of the amount of heat given out during this very EXOTHERMIC demonstration.

The cyclohexanol is poured into the gas jar, and the starting temperature read from the thermometer (which in this demonstration was 20°C). All of the nitric acid is then added as quickly as possible because the reaction is violent and all hands need to be clear of the apparatus by the time the reaction starts (②).

Within a few seconds the reaction produces a 'volcanic' eruption of bubbling liquid and a gush of brown smoke (③ & ④). As the bubbling subsides and the gas clears, the temperature of the thermometer is read again (⑤). In this demonstration the reading was 110°C.

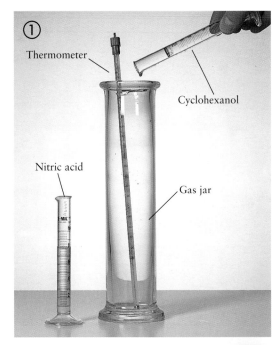

① Thermometer — Cyclohexanol — Nitric acid — Gas jar

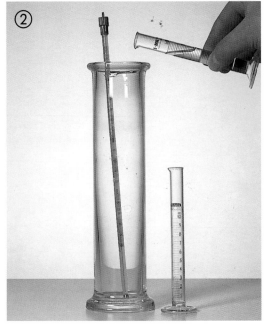

②

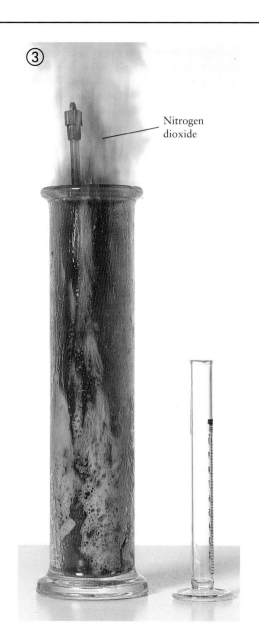

Nitrogen
dioxide

EQUATION: The oxidation of cyclohexanol

Cyclohexanol + concentrated nitric acid ⇨ nitrogen dioxide + hexandioic acid + water

$C_6H_{11}OH(l) + 8HNO_3(conc) ⇨ 8NO_2(g) + HOOC(CH_2)_4COOH(l) + 5H_2O(l)$

Heat given out

Distillation of ethanoic acid

Ethanol (C_2H_5OH) is the most important commercial alcohol. In this demonstration it will be oxidised to ethanoic acid (CH_3COOH). Ethanoic acid is also called acetic acid, and it is the main acid found in vinegar.

Demonstration: preparation and simple distillation of ethanoic acid

The apparatus used in this demonstration consists of a flask and a REFLUX DISTILLATION SYSTEM. A reflux distillation system uses a LIEBIG CONDENSER placed vertically, so that all the vapours created during boiling are condensed back into the liquid, rather than escaping as vapour. In this way, the concentration of all the reactants remains constant.

The oxidising agent to be used in this demonstration is potassium dichromate. The potassium dichromate is first put in a flask (①), and acidified with a small amount of concentrated sulphuric acid. Ethanol is now poured into the flask (②). The liquid mixture is bright orange due to the chromium(VI) ions of the dichromate. The mixture is then heated so that oxidation can proceed more rapidly (③).

As the ethanol is oxidised (④), the potassium dichromate is reduced and the orange chromium(VI) ions are reduced to blue chromium(III) ions. While there are both kinds of coloured ion in the solution, the result is to turn the solution a deep green colour. Because excess oxidising agent is used, even at the end of the demonstration (which takes about half an hour to get to

① Potassium dichromate crystals

Funnel

Flask

② Concentrated sulphuric acid and then ethanol are added.

③

Bunsen flame

completion), there will be both orange and blue chromium ions and so the colour will remain green (⑤).

The second stage is to separate the ethanoic acid from the rest of the liquid mixture. This is achieved by SIMPLE DISTILLATION (⑥).

Simple distillation uses the same distillation glassware as in the reflux stage of the demonstration, only rearranged horizontally. In this case, when the liquid mixture is heated and vapours are produced, they enter the condenser and then flow away from the flask and can be collected.

Remarks

When the mixture is heated in the second stage of the demonstration, aqueous ethanoic acid, rather than pure ethanoic acid, is distilled. This is because ethanoic acid boils at 118°C and water boils at 100°C. These values are too close to separate with simple distillation apparatus.

Natural oxidation of ethanol takes place in alcoholic liquids such as wine when they are left open to the air and the ethanol changes to ethanoic acid. This is why a wine that has not been properly sealed tastes sour.

As the ethanol is oxidised to ethanoic acid, the dichromate is reduced to chromium(III) ions, changing the colour of the solution. Both ethanol and ethanoic acid are colourless.

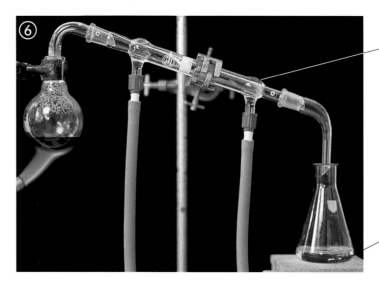

Ethanoic acid vapour is condensed in the cold water-cooled Liebig condenser.

The colourless ethanoic acid liquid is collected in a flask.

EQUATION: Oxidising ethanol to ethanoic acid
Ethanol + oxygen from the dichromate(VI) ⇨ ethanoic acid + water
$C_2H_5OH(aq) + O_2(aq) \Rightarrow CH_3OOH(aq) + H_2O(l)$

Separation of crude oil by fractional distillation

Fractional distillation is a technique used to separate complex liquid mixtures, many of which are VOLATILE. It is most commonly used to separate the many FRACTIONS (parts of the mixture) in petroleum.

Petroleum contains liquids, solids and dissolved gases. These can each be separated by progressive heating of the mixture. If the boiling point of each fraction is known, then the temperature in the distillation flask can be raised in stages to the boiling point of each fraction in turn. The vapour produced can then be distilled and collected (①).

Demonstration: fractional distillation of crude oil

FRACTIONAL DISTILLATION can only be done with a special piece of apparatus called a fractionating column (②). This might be a column filled with beads or a glass spiral that is placed above the heated liquid (③).

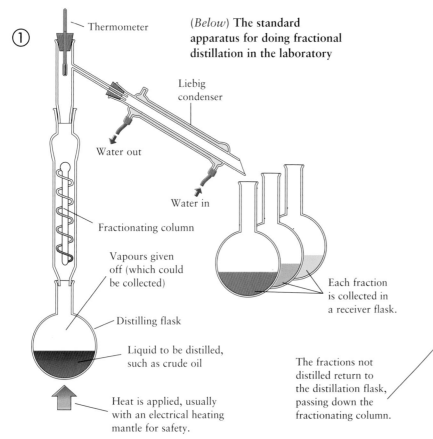

① Thermometer

(*Below*) **The standard apparatus for doing fractional distillation in the laboratory**

Liebig condenser

Water out

Water in

Fractionating column

Vapours given off (which could be collected)

Distilling flask

Liquid to be distilled, such as crude oil

Heat is applied, usually with an electrical heating mantle for safety.

Each fraction is collected in a receiver flask.

The fractions not distilled return to the distillation flask, passing down the fractionating column.

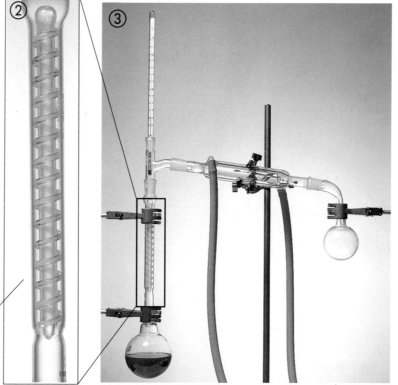

The mixture is heated just sufficiently to cause the most volatile fraction in the remaining liquid to boil off and to make its vapours flow through the column and then be condensed and collected (④). Any heavier vapours that have evaporated as well, cool before they reach the top of the column, condense, and pass back down to the original liquid.

The temperature is then raised in order to collect the next most volatile fraction. At each stage, the chosen temperature is kept constant by observing the thermometer above the fractionating column and varying the heat applied to the mixture (⑤).

Remarks

The more volatile fractions that are collected at the lower temperatures are called 'light fractions'. The higher the temperature that the crude oil is heated to, the darker the colour of the fraction that is collected.

Fractions collected at the higher temperatures are called 'heavy fractions'. In all cases the fractions are noticeably lighter in colour when compared to the original mixture, which itself gets progressively darker with heating.

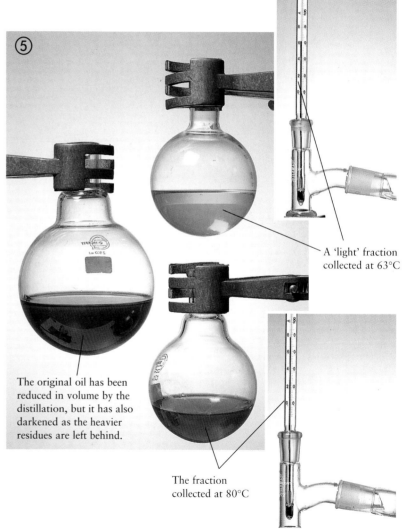

⑤

A 'light' fraction collected at 63°C

The original oil has been reduced in volume by the distillation, but it has also darkened as the heavier residues are left behind.

The fraction collected at 80°C

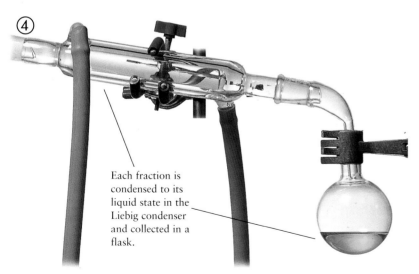

④

Each fraction is condensed to its liquid state in the Liebig condenser and collected in a flask.

Cracking a hydrocarbon in the laboratory

One of the products of fractional distillation of crude petroleum is long chain hydrocarbons. These have a very limited industrial use. Heating over a suitable surface causes these molecules to crack (break down) into smaller, more useful ones. The process of thermal cracking is also known as pyrolysis.

Demonstration: cracking of engine oil

The apparatus consists of a boiling tube, at the far end of which is some mineral wool that has been soaked in an oily hydrocarbon, in this case, engine oil (①). Some ceramic chips are placed about half-way along the tube, and a stopper and delivery tube fitted. The delivery tube leads down to a pneumatic trough and a boiling tube is used to collect the gases that result from the cracking.

In this demonstration, the ceramic chips are used as a hot surface. The ceramic chips are heated using a Bunsen flame and, as they heat up, the heat causes some of the oily hydrocarbon to vaporise. Some of the vapour then flows over the hot ceramic chips, where it is cracked into smaller molecules of ethene gas.

You can see the progress of the cracking because the ceramic chips gradually become covered in a black deposit as the demonstration proceeds (②, ③ & ④, see pages 37 and 38).

The ethene gas is collected over water in a boiling tube. Once the tube is full and gas begins to bubble from around the edges of the tube, the delivery tube is removed from the pneumatic trough, and a lighted splint applied to the end. The gas immediately begins to burn with a smoky yellow (hydrocarbon) flame (⑤, see page 39). (The delivery tube must also be removed from the water to prevent water being sucked back into the hot boiling tube and causing an explosion.)

①

Colourless ethene gas

Several test tubes are prepared. They are first filled with water and inverted so that the gas can be collected over water.

Ceramic chips

Delivery tube

Heat is applied using a Bunsen burner.

Mineral wool soaked in engine oil

Pneumatic trough filled with cold water

The collected gas can be identified by a test using bromine water. The bromine water is poured into a test tube containing the ethene (⑥, see page 39). The reaction produces a colourless liquid (⑦ & ⑧). This is a standard test for unsaturated hydrocarbon compounds, of which ethene is one of the most common.

Remarks

Ethene is a MONOMER that can be used to manufacture polyethene (polythene). There is also a brown liquid produced, which makes an oily layer on the surface of the water in the pneumatic trough. This is made of a mixture of heavier molecules that have condensed in the delivery tube.

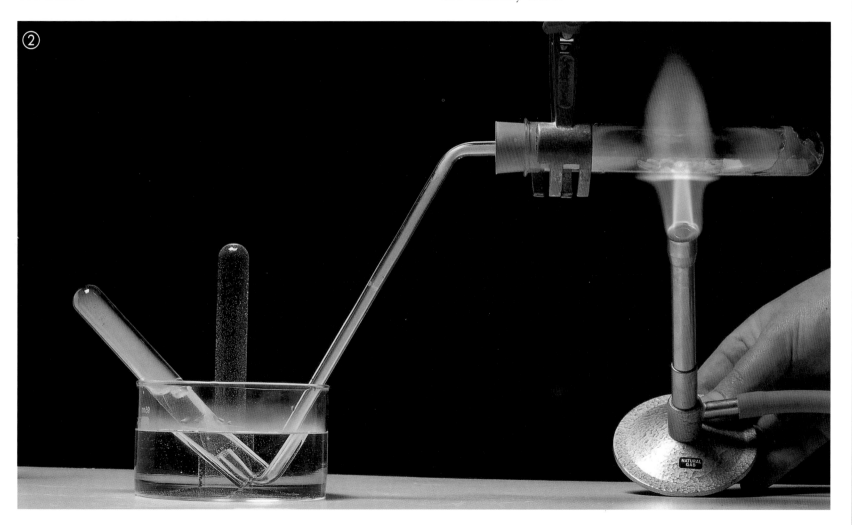

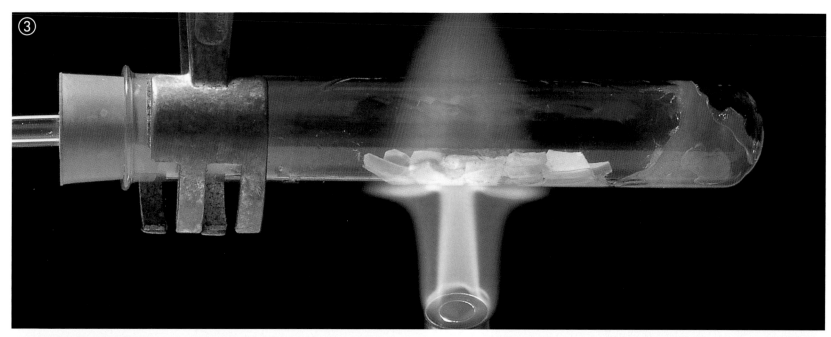

The ceramic chips have also become blackened. This is the result of carbon being deposited on them. In an industrial apparatus, the catalytic surface would become useless due to the build-up of a carbon deposit, and so methods have to be found to remove the carbon so that the efficiency of the apparatus is not impaired.

Catalytic cracking

In this demonstration, which is known as thermal cracking, a large area of ceramic chips is used to cause the breakdown of the hydrocarbon. It is possible to use a mixture of aluminium oxide and silica oxide as a CATALYST instead of the ceramic chips. This is known as catalytic cracking. Using a catalyst like this not only breaks down the hydrocarbons, but promotes the formation of carbon ions. Catalysts are used in industrial cracking of hydrocarbons (see page 24).

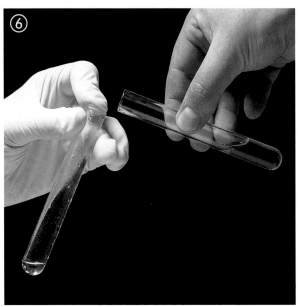

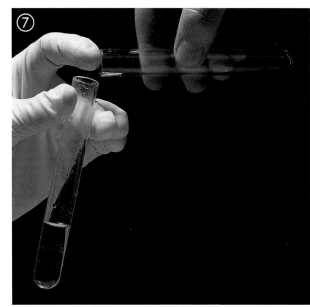

Pyrolysis of wood

Wood is a complex organic substance that decomposes, when heated, into a variety of materials. Wood pyrolysis (cracking, or heating the wood in such a way that it breaks down into liquids and gases) was once used on a large industrial scale to produce methanol, also called wood alcohol.

Demonstration: destructive distillation of wood

The apparatus consists of a tin with a close-fitting lid (①). A small hole is made in the lid of the tin, and the tin is then half filled with sawdust (wood with a large surface area). The tin is then placed on a tripod and heated strongly using a Bunsen flame.

The tin heats quickly and a smoky gas appears through the hole (②). Putting a Bunsen flame to this gas does not cause ignition, proving that it is non-combustible. In fact, it is mostly steam.

The steam then stops, and the gases coming from the hole now combust to provide a long jet of smoky yellow flame (③). The first combustible gases are therefore hydrocarbons of low molecular weight, and are the most volatile of the components remaining in the wood. As burning progresses, the flame becomes less yellow and begins to lose its colour, suggesting that the vapour being burned contains more alcohol than hydrocarbon substances.

After a few minutes, the gases cease as all of the gaseous components have been burned off. When the tin is allowed to cool and the lid opened, an oily deposit is found on the inside of the tin (④). These are the heavy molecular substances which were not volatile enough to be emitted as gases but were simply distilled out of the wood and then condensed in the tin.

The black powder making up the bulk of the remaining material in the tin is charcoal (black carbon).

Remarks

The pyrolysis of wood distils out all of the hydrogen-containing components of the wood, either as steam or as hydrocarbon gases and alcohols.

④

Pyrolysis of coal

Pyrolysis (cracking or destructive distillation) of coal is an important industrial process once used to produce gas supplies. As the coal is heated strongly, it breaks down into a wide range of liquids and gases. Here, the first stages of pyrolysis of coal are examined by heating coal in a boiling tube.

Demonstration: destructive distillation of coal

This demonstration uses powdered bituminous coal. To obtain the powder, lumps of coal are ground down with a pestle and mortar, and the powder is scattered along the boiling tube using a spatula (①).

The gases from the pyrolysis are carried along a delivery tube to another boiling tube, which is kept upright in a beaker of cold water. The purpose of this arrangement is to cause the condensation of some vapours produced during the pyrolysis. The entry tube goes close to the bottom of the boiling tube, the exit tube is close to the top.

The exit tube from the condensing system is taken to a gas jar and pneumatic trough, so that gases can be collected over water.

Once the coal powder has been added and the stopper fitted in place, the coal is heated very strongly (②). The products of the pyrolysis depend on the strength of the heating (③). If the heat is sufficient, the pyrolysis goes to completion and the material

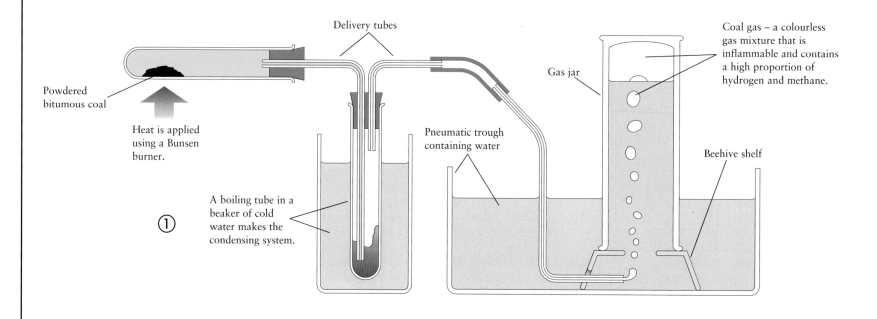

Powdered bitumous coal

Heat is applied using a Bunsen burner.

Delivery tubes

A boiling tube in a beaker of cold water makes the condensing system.

①

Pneumatic trough containing water

Gas jar

Coal gas – a colourless gas mixture that is inflammable and contains a high proportion of hydrogen and methane.

Beehive shelf

remaining in the boiling tube is carbon powder. If the heating is not sufficiently strong to allow the reactions to go to completion, then the material remaining in the boiling tube is smokeless fuel.

As the pyrolysis proceeds (④, see page 44), the boiling tube containing the coal fills with a peach-coloured, steamy vapour (⑤). This moves through the delivery tube to the condensing system, where two layers of liquid collect: some dark, peach-coloured, tarry-looking material and some yellow, watery material (⑥, see page 45).

The gas that collects in the gas jar is mostly coal gas, which is inflammable and contains a high proportion of hydrogen and methane, but also other gases such as carbon monoxide and hydrogen sulphide. The inflammable nature of the gas can be tested with a lighted splint at the end of the demonstration (⑦).

Remarks

Coal tar products (those of high molecular weight that are condensed) were used in the production of the first synthetic dyes.

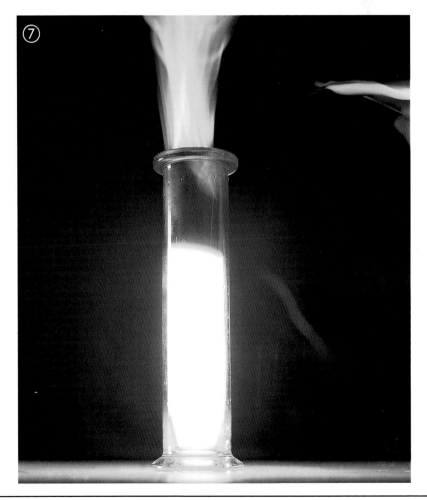

Separating organic materials using separating columns

This demonstration shows how an inert substance, aluminium oxide, can be used as a selective filter for separating a complex mixture, such as natural juice from plants.

Demonstration: separating beetroot juice

Small amounts of a complex organic mixture can often be separated into its components using a SEPARATING COLUMN. The main piece of apparatus is a long glass tube (the separating column) with a porous disc fixed across the tube close to the bottom, and a tap to control the flow of liquid from it. The disc allows liquids to pass through, but will hold back all solids (①).

The separating column is stood upright in a clamp. An organic solvent such as propanone (acetone) is poured into the column (②). The purpose of the solvent is to provide a liquid into which aluminium oxide powder can settle.

The aluminium oxide powder is now poured into the column slowly and carefully (③). The success of separation depends not only on the aluminium oxide having special surface properties that will hold back some of the fractions of a mixture, while allowing others to flow more rapidly through, but also on the fact that even packing allows each fraction to move through the column in a controlled way. It is therefore

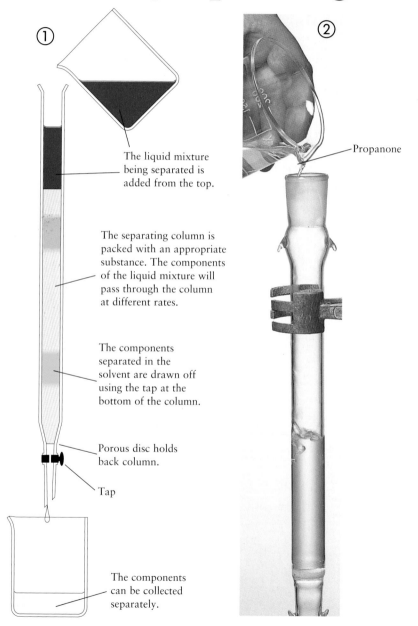

①

The liquid mixture being separated is added from the top.

The separating column is packed with an appropriate substance. The components of the liquid mixture will pass through the column at different rates.

The components separated in the solvent are drawn off using the tap at the bottom of the column.

Porous disc holds back column.

Tap

The components can be collected separately.

②

Propanone

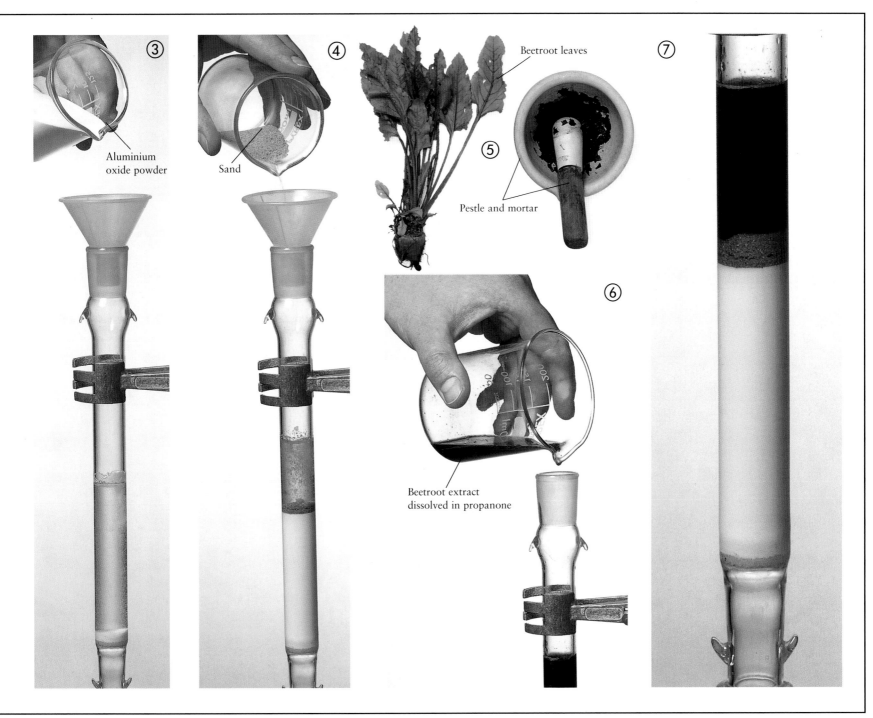

③ Aluminium oxide powder

④ Sand

Beetroot leaves

⑤ Pestle and mortar

⑥ Beetroot extract dissolved in propanone

⑦

vital that the powder is introduced slowly and carefully so that it settles evenly at the bottom, building up a column of uniform density and pore space.

When the column has been filled sufficiently with aluminium oxide, a thin layer of sand is poured on to the top to provide a 'cushion' between the liquid being poured in and the carefully packed column of powder (④, see page 47).

The liquid to be separated is now poured into the top of the column (which in this case is beetroot extract) (⑤, ⑥ & ⑦, see page 47). The tap at the base of the column is turned, allowing the liquid to pass through the column.

As the extract passes through the aluminium oxide, the fractions separate because they move at different rates. Many of the fractions have their own colour (which together contribute to the deep red of the beetroot juice) and thus the colours relating to each component of the mixture appear as a number of coloured bands (⑧ & ⑨).

As soon as the extract has flowed completely into the aluminium oxide, more propanone is added to help flush all of the extract through the column (⑩, ⑪ & ⑫).

Small beakers are placed below the column so that the fractions can be collected in turn (⑬ & ⑭).

Remarks

Each of the fractions has its own solubility in the propanone and its own tendency to be adsorbed on the solid surface, and this determines the order in which fractions flow through the column.

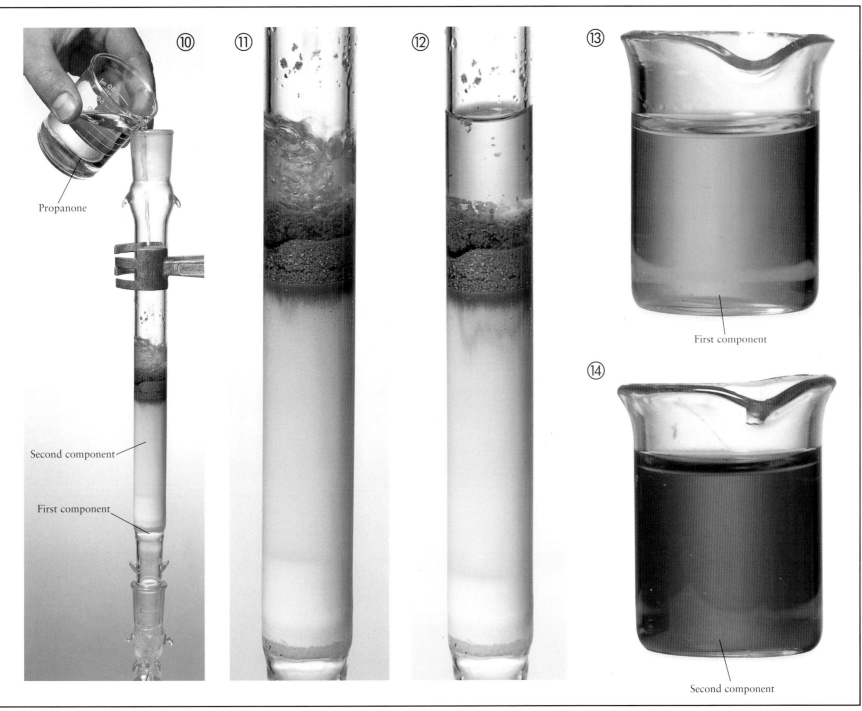

⑩

Propanone

Second component

First component

⑪

⑫

⑬

First component

⑭

Second component

The efficiency of alcohol fuels

Many organic compounds can be used as fuels. Some of the fuels that are most inflammable are the alcohols because they have an oxygen atom within their structure and so can be partly self-oxidising. The oxygen in the alcohols also explains why they burn with an almost colourless (i.e. soot-free) flame.

Methanol, ethanol, propanol and butanol are alcohols used as fuels. This apparatus is designed to investigate which of them is the most efficient as a fuel in terms of kilojoules of heat released per gram of fuel.

Demonstration: comparison of three alcohols

The apparatus consists of a burner containing the fuel under test, and a beaker of water together with a stirring thermometer. The whole apparatus is shielded from draughts by a cylinder of transparent plastic. The cylinder has slots cut in its lower end to allow the free passage of air (①).

The whole burner, including fuel is first weighed. The beaker is then filled with a known volume of water, say 40 cm³, and the initial temperature recorded. The burner is lit (②) and kept alight until the thermometer reads some specified value, for example, 20°C above its starting value (③). The burner is extinguished and then reweighed so that the amount of fuel used can be measured accurately.

The demonstration is then repeated exactly using each of the fuels under test in turn (④).

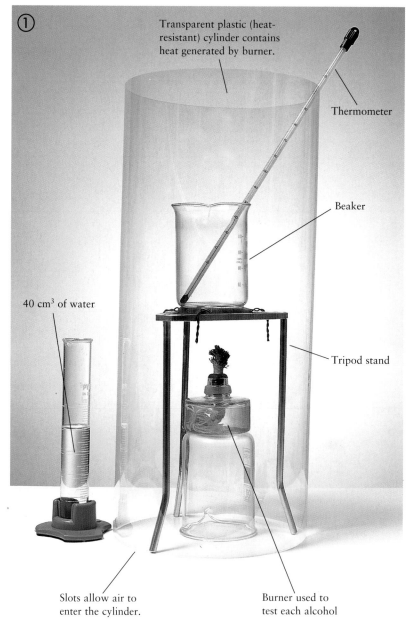

① Transparent plastic (heat-resistant) cylinder contains heat generated by burner.

Thermometer

Beaker

40 cm³ of water

Tripod stand

Slots allow air to enter the cylinder.

Burner used to test each alcohol

② 40 cm³ of water is placed in beaker.

③

Type of fuel used	Mass of fuel used
Methanol	1.3 g
Ethanol	1.5 g
Propanol	1.7 g
Butanol	2.0 g

Demonstrating that carbohydrates contain carbon, hydrogen and oxygen

Carbohydrates are a very important group of organic compounds. They contain carbon, and hydrogen and oxygen. Carbohydrates contain the elements of water. As a result, they can be DEHYDRATED using a strong dehydrating agent such as concentrated sulphuric acid. This can be demonstrated by dehydrating sucrose ($C_{12}H_{22}O_{11}$).

Demonstration: dehydration of sucrose using concentrated sulphuric acid

Some sugar is placed in a boiling tube, and concentrated sulphuric acid is added (①). The sugar becomes liquid, turning first yellow (②), then brown (③) and finally black (④). After a few moments, the surface of the liquid bulges up and cracks (⑤). By now, so much heat is given out that much of the surplus water produced by the dehydration reaction forms steam. However, the steam bubbles are trapped in the sticky black product and so the steam remains trapped, creating a froth (⑥ & ⑦). When the reaction is over, and the heat subsides, the frothed carbon sets hard like a piece of coke (⑧).

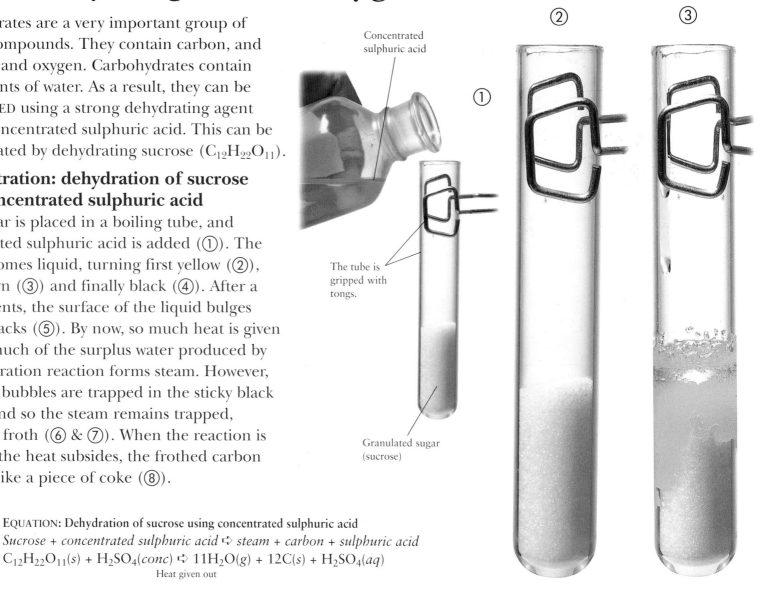

Concentrated sulphuric acid

① ② ③

The tube is gripped with tongs.

Granulated sugar (sucrose)

EQUATION: Dehydration of sucrose using concentrated sulphuric acid

Sucrose + concentrated sulphuric acid ⇨ steam + carbon + sulphuric acid

$C_{12}H_{22}O_{11}(s) + H_2SO_4(conc) ⇨ 11H_2O(g) + 12C(s) + H_2SO_4(aq)$

Heat given out

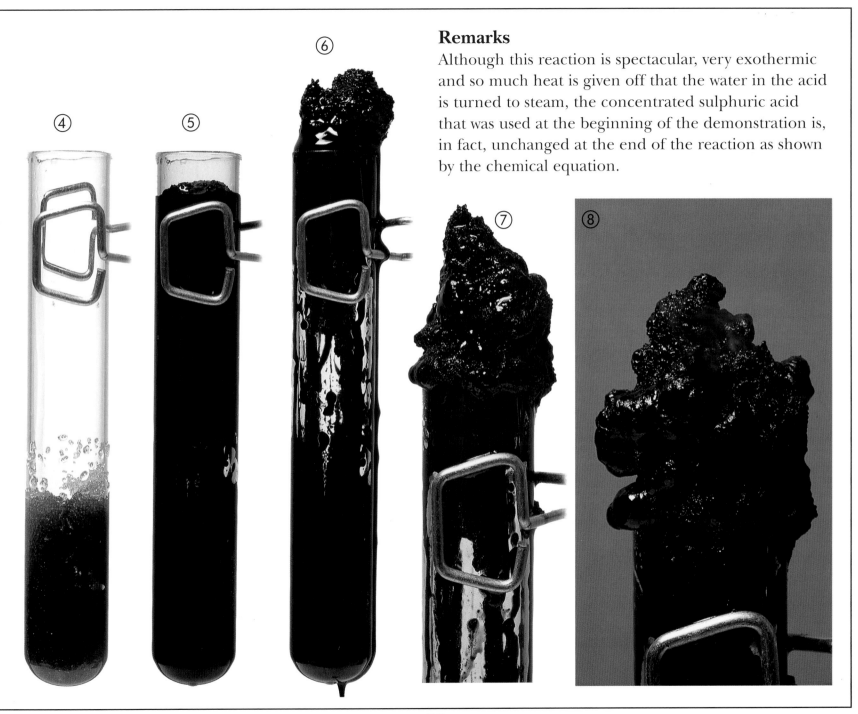

④ ⑤ ⑥ ⑦ ⑧

Remarks

Although this reaction is spectacular, very exothermic and so much heat is given off that the water in the acid is turned to steam, the concentrated sulphuric acid that was used at the beginning of the demonstration is, in fact, unchanged at the end of the reaction as shown by the chemical equation.

Sugars as reducing agents

Sugars are carbohydrates (see page 52) some of which, under certain circumstances, can be used as reducing agents. This demonstration shows how a metal can be made to precipitate out as a thin film on the inside of a clean, grease-free flask using a reducing sugar. The same demonstration can also be used as a test for a reducing sugar.

Demonstration: using glucose to reduce silver nitrate

This demonstration uses a long-necked, round-bottomed flask to make it easier to swirl the liquid around and get an even metallic coating. The flask must first be cleaned thoroughly and degreased using concentrated nitric acid and then distilled water.

Silver nitrate solution is now poured into the flask. Sodium hydroxide solution is then added to produce a precipitate of silver oxide (①).

Ammonia solution is next added (②) until the precipitate begins to 'redissolve' (the precipitate reacts with the ammonia to form a soluble product diamminesilver(I) ions – $Ag(NH_3)_2^+(aq)$).

As the contents of the flask are swirled around, it becomes possible to see whether enough ammonia has been added. If a solid precipitate can be seen, more

Sodium hydroxide

② Ammonia solution

③

④ Glucose solution

① Silver nitrate solution (colourless)

Brown silver oxide precipitated

ammonia needs to be added (③). Finally, a clear solution is obtained.

The next step is to use the reducing agent – in this case, a solution of glucose in water. The glucose solution is added from a pipette (④).

Reduction of the diamminesilver(I) ions to silver produces some black metal particles suspended in the solution (⑤). At the same time, a silver 'mirror' (a thin film) begins to form on the inner surface of the flask. It tends to form at a small number of places and then grow outwards from these starting points (⑥).

Once the mirror has started to form, the contents are allowed to stand so that natural precipitation processes can produce a film over the entire surface (⑦).

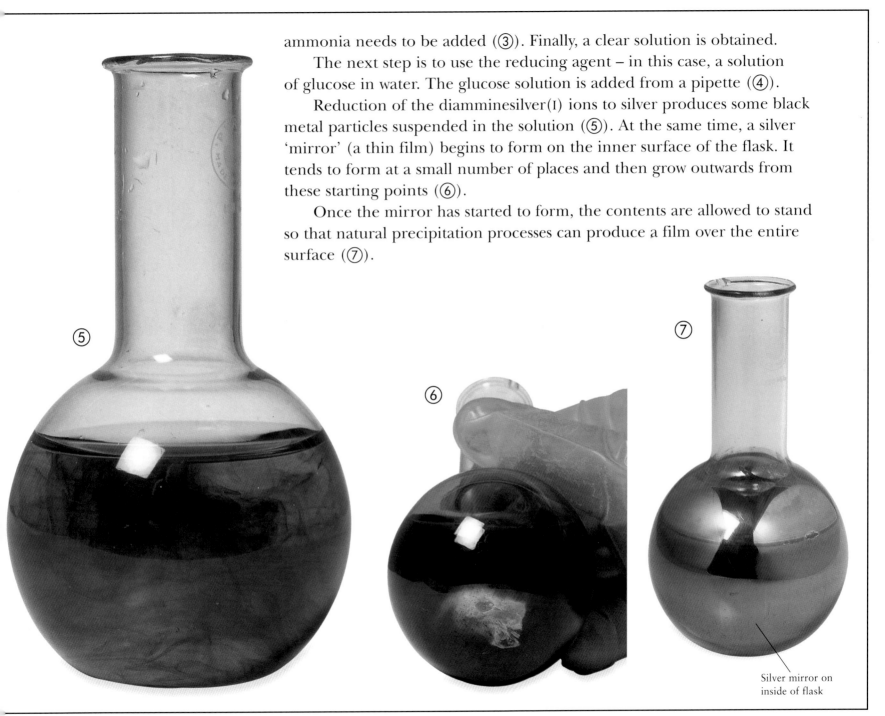

Silver mirror on inside of flask

POLYMERS

A POLYMER is a material made from many identical molecules (monomers) that have linked together into a chain to make a giant molecule.

Natural polymers include cellulose and rubber, while synthetic polymers include plastics, synthetic rubbers, synthetic fibres such as rayon and nylon, adhesives and paints.

Polymers are giant molecules. They form in two ways, by addition and by condensation of thousands of individual monomers.

Addition polymerisation

This form of polymerisation occurs when an unsaturated hydrocarbon with a double bond breaks open, so that one bond can be used to link to other molecules. Ethene is a widely used monomer that forms polymers by addition.

The chemical formula of an addition polymer is almost identical to that of the monomers from which it is formed.

Condensation polymerisation

The alternative to addition polymerisation is called condensation polymerisation. This is more like a chemical reaction between reactants, and the chemical formula of the polymer is not the same as the chemical formula of the molecules from which is was formed. In this process, each stage in the polymer chain forms as a water molecule is expelled. It is the expulsion of water that gives this form of polymerisation its name. A much wider range of

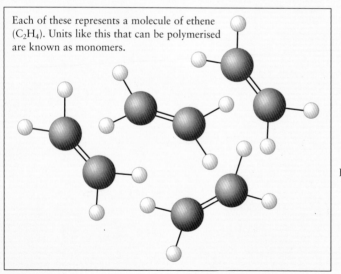

Each of these represents a molecule of ethene (C_2H_4). Units like this that can be polymerised are known as monomers.

Polymerisation

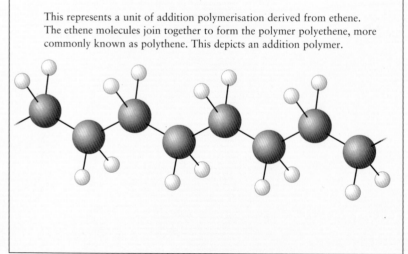

This represents a unit of addition polymerisation derived from ethene. The ethene molecules join together to form the polymer polyethene, more commonly known as polythene. This depicts an addition polymer.

polymers can be made from condensation polymerisation than from addition polymerisation.

Many common fibres are formed by condensation polymerisation, including nylon (see page 62) and polyester.

Thermoplastic and thermosetting polymers

Polymers can have one of two fundamental properties. They can be of the kind that can be heated, remoulded and then cooled repeatedly. These are called thermoplastic polymers. The forces between the chains are weak, allowing the material to be heated, remoulded and cooled time after time.

Addition polymers such as polyethene (polythene), that become soft on heating and harden on cooling time after time, are thermoplastic polymers.

The other main group of plastics are thermosetting polymers (see page 64). These can be heated and moulded once only. Once they have set, they cannot be resoftened. In this case, the force of attraction between the polymer chains is strong and, on heating, they build up cross-links, to form a single giant structure which cannot be changed by subsequent reheating. The thermosetting polymers include epoxy-resins, Bakelite and others made from phenol and methanal (formaldehyde).

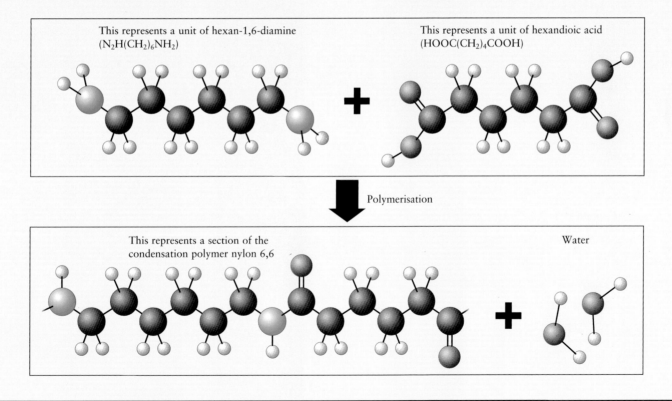

This represents a unit of hexan-1,6-diamine ($N_2H(CH_2)_6NH_2$)

This represents a unit of hexandioic acid ($HOOC(CH_2)_4COOH$)

Polymerisation

This represents a section of the condensation polymer nylon 6,6

Water

Making rayon

Natural polymers include the plant fibre, cellulose. One of the products that can be obtained from cellulose is rayon, whose preparation is demonstrated below. Rayon is a condensation polymer.

Demonstration: making rayon from filter paper

A mixture of copper(II) carbonate and concentrated ammonia solution is first made up (①). This produces indigo blue tetraamminecopper(II), which has the ability to dissolve cellulose.

The source of cellulose for this demonstration is filter paper. The filter paper is cut into strips and simply stirred into the solution of tetraamminecopper(II) (②), whereupon it dissolves within a few seconds (③).

A small quantity of the dissolved cellulose can now be sucked into a pipette and then transferred to a Petri dish containing a shallow layer of dilute sulphuric acid (④). A small part of the dissolved solution can be squirted into the Petri dish, taking care to make sure the pipette does not move. Rayon is precipitated immediately. As the rayon precipitates, it has to be trapped against the glass bottom of the Petri dish.

Once trapped, the pipette can then be drawn slowly through the acid, squeezing gently on the bulb at the same time, so that a long filament of rayon is produced (⑤).

① Glass stirring rod — Concentrated ammonia solution — Copper carbonate

② Deep blue coloured tetraamminecopper(II) — Filter paper

③ Filter paper is dissolved in tetraamminecopper(II) solution.

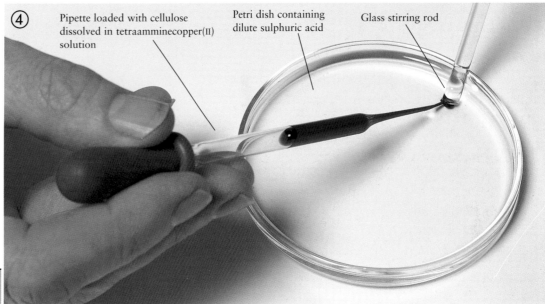

④ Pipette loaded with cellulose dissolved in tetraamminecopper(II) solution

Petri dish containing dilute sulphuric acid

Glass stirring rod

(Above) This photograph shows the tetraamminecopper(II) solution being poured into the funnel. The filter paper dissolves immediately, leaving a large hole.

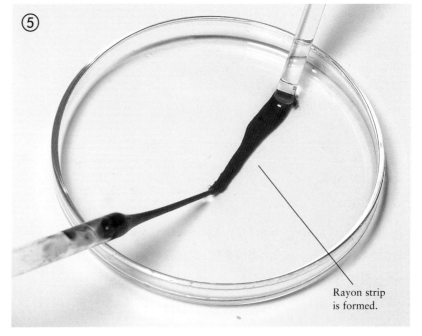

⑤

Rayon strip is formed.

The thread is strong enough to be lifted from the acid bath as shown in the last pictures of this sequence (⑥, ⑦ & ⑧).

This thread is blue initially, but within a few minutes the thread loses its colour and a colourless strand remains (⑨).

Remarks

Filter paper is used rather than writing paper because it is free from the clays and other contaminating materials, designed to give writing paper a smooth finish.

The industrial process that produces rayon in factories begins with a solution containing dissolved cellulose which is squeezed, rather than pulled, through a nozzle containing many small holes. This device, a spinneret, produces long threads of cellulose (rayon), which can be precipitated by running them through an acid bath.

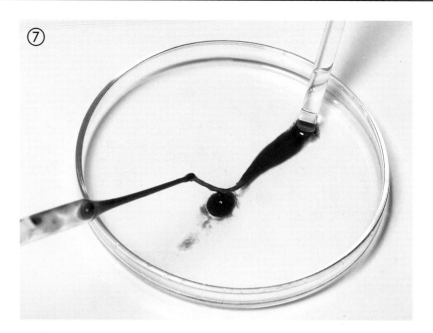

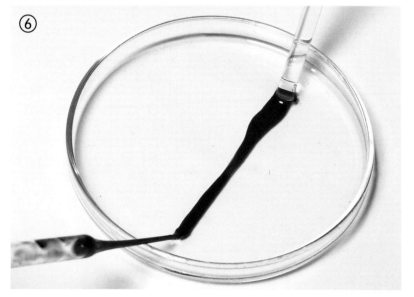

(Below) A diagrammatic representation of a section of rayon. The rayon polymer can be made of up to 270 glucose units derived from the cellulose.

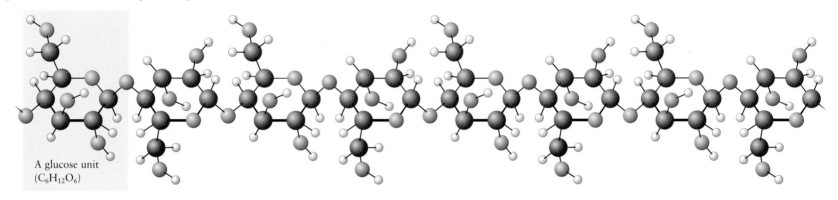

A glucose unit
$(C_6H_{12}O_6)$

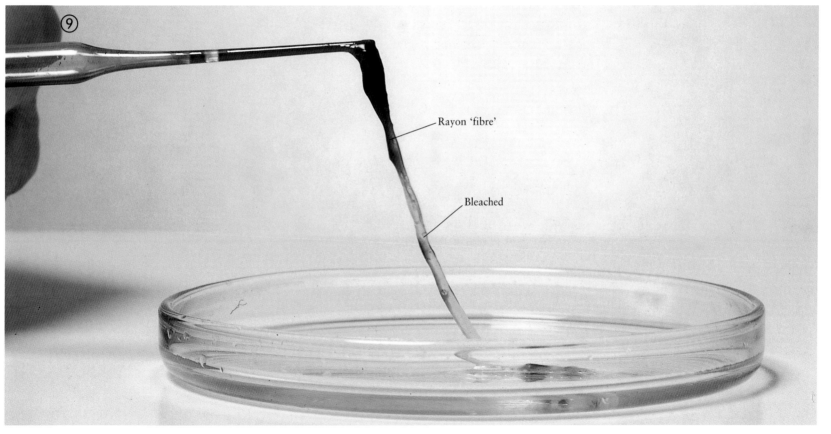

Rayon 'fibre'

Bleached

Making nylon

The first fibre made from natural polymers was rayon, a treated form of natural plant cellulose (see page 58). The first entirely synthetic fibre was made in 1938 and called nylon.

Demonstration: making nylon from hexan-1,6-diamine and hexan-dioyl chloride

This demonstration uses two organic chemicals hexan-1,6-diamine and hexan-dioyl chloride. The apparatus is simply a beaker and a glass stirring rod.

The hexan-1,6-diamine in solution in water is poured into the beaker and the hexan-dioyl chloride is poured on top of it (①). The liquids are not MISCIBLE and so they form two layers. However, they react along the surface where they meet to form a white solid (②). This is nylon.

The technique of extruding the nylon from the liquids and forming into a thread takes some practice. A piece of the nylon is picked out of the solution using tongs (③) and is lifted clear carefully and steadily (④). If the nylon is pulled too fast, the filament will break, but if it is pulled too slowly, then it will thicken. This picture shows the typical result of pulling a thread. The uneven diameter (⑤) shows clearly.

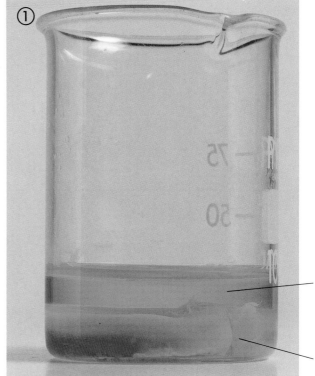

Hexan-dioyl chloride

Hexan-1,6-diamine

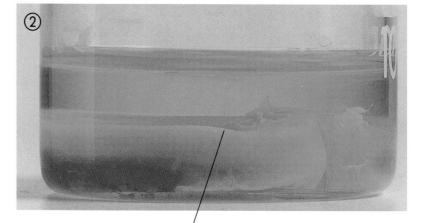

Here you can see the nylon forming at the interface between the two liquids.

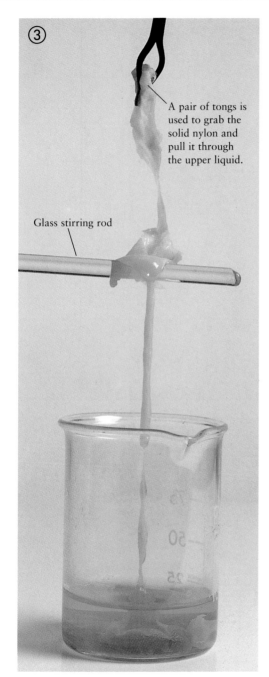

③ A pair of tongs is used to grab the solid nylon and pull it through the upper liquid.

Glass stirring rod

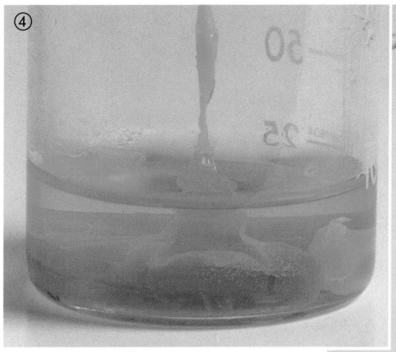

④

⑤

Nylon 'thread'

Remarks

The filament can only be produced while the two liquids remain in contact. As soon as the batch of reactants is used up, a new filament has to be picked from a new batch of reactants. Clearly, while the laboratory process shows that it is possible to produce filaments easily, industrial processes have to be found that make a more reliable filament in a continuous process. To do this, the two reactants are introduced continuously and the threads are extruded, not drawn.

The thermosetting properties of polymers

A hard, white thermosetting condensation polymer can be produced by adding concentrated sulphuric acid to a mixture of formaldehyde and urea.

Demonstration: making a thermoset polymer

The urea and formaldehyde crystals are mixed together in a disposable glass jar (the remains of the unused polymer will set in the jar, and so the jar cannot be reused) (①).

The sulphuric acid is then added slowly and the solution stirred. Within a few seconds the solution turns cloudy. Considerable heat is evolved, showing this to be an exothermic reaction.

If the polymer is to be poured into a container, such as the aluminium pie dish shown in this demonstration, then the solution must be poured quickly before it sets to a hard white solid (②, ③ & ④).

As soon as the polymer is hard, as tested with a spatula (⑤), the aluminium container can be peeled away, leaving the polymer, which takes on the exact shape of the container (⑥).

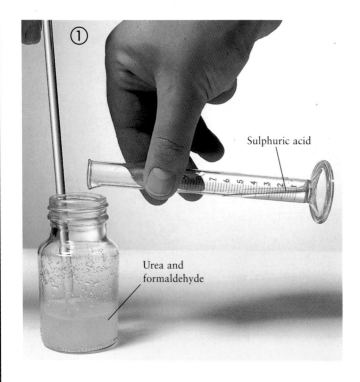

Sulphuric acid

Urea and formaldehyde

Aluminium pie dish

Polymer

Part, or all, of the polymer can then be held in metal tongs and exposed to a Bunsen flame (⑦). The polymer does not melt, but remains a white solid, heating to red-hot and then charring, as seen by the blackened edges.

Remarks

Speed is of the essence when pouring the polymer or there is a danger that the solution will set while it is being poured and resemble a stalactite!

MASTER GLOSSARY

absolute zero: the lowest possible temperature ($-273.15°C$).

absorption: the process by which a substance is soaked up. *See:* adsorption.

acid: a substance that can give a proton to another substance. Acids are compounds, containing hydrogen, that can attack and dissolve many substances. Acids are described as weak or strong, dilute or concentrated, mineral or organic. *Example:* hydrochloric acid (HCl). An acid in water can react with a base to form a salt and water.

acidic solution: a solution with a pH lower than 7.

acidity: a general term for the strength of an acid in a solution.

acid radical: the negative ion left behind when an acid loses a hydrogen ion. *Example:* Cl^- in hydrochloric acid (HCl).

acid salt: An ACID SALT contains at least one hydrogen ion and can behave as an acid in chemical reactions. Acid salts are produced under conditions that do not allow complete neutralisation of the acid. For example, sulphuric acid may react with a sodium compound to produce a normal sodium salt, sodium sulphate (Na_2SO_4), or it may retain some of the hydrogen, in which case it becomes the salt sodium hydrogen sulphate ($NaHSO_4$).

actinide series or actinide metals: a series of 15 similar radioactive elements between actinium and lawrencium. They are transition metals.

activated charcoal: a form of carbon, made up of tiny crystals of graphite, which is made by heating organic matter in the absence of air. It is then processed further to increase its pore space and therefore its surface area. Its surface area is about $2000\ m^2/g$. Activated charcoal readily adsorbs many gases and it is therefore widely used as a filter, for example, in gas masks.

activation energy: the energy required to make a reaction occur. The greater the activation energy of a reaction, the more its reaction rate depends on temperature. The activation energy of a reaction is useful because, if the rate of reaction is known at one temperature (for example, $100\ °C$) then the activation energy can be used to calculate the rate of reaction at another temperature (for example, $400\ °C$) without actually doing the experiment.

adsorption: the process by which a surface adsorbs a substance. The substances involved are not chemically combined and can be separated. *Example:* the adsorption properties of activated charcoal. *See:* absorption.

alchemy: the traditional 'art' of working with chemicals that prevailed through the Middle Ages. One of the main challenges for alchemists was to make gold from lead. Alchemy faded away as scientific chemistry was developed in the 17th century.

alcohol: an organic compound which contains a hydroxyl (OH) group. *Example:* ethanol (CH_3CH_2OH), also known as ethyl alcohol or grain alcohol.

alkali/alkaline: a base in (aqueous) solution. Alkalis react with, or neutralise, hydrogen ions in acids and have a pH greater than 7.0 because they contain relatively few hydrogen ions. *Example:* aqueous sodium hydroxide (NaOH).

alkaline cell (or battery): a dry cell in which the electrolyte contains sodium or potassium hydroxide.

alkaline earth metal: a member of Group 2 of the Periodic Table. *Example:* calcium.

alkali metals: a member of Group 1 of the Periodic Table. *Example:* sodium.

alkane: a hydrocarbon with no carbon-to-carbon multiple bonds. *Example:* ethane, C_2H_6.

alkene: a hydrocarbon with at least one carbon-to-carbon double bond. *Example:* ethene, C_2H_4.

alkyne: a hydrocarbon with at least one carbon-to-carbon triple bond. *Example:* ethyne, C_2H_2.

allotropes: alternative forms of an element that differ in the way the atoms are linked. *Example:* white and red phosphorus.

alloy: a mixture of a metal and various other elements. *Example:* brass is an alloy of copper and zinc.

amalgam: a liquid alloy of mercury with another metal.

amorphous: a solid in which the atoms are not arranged regularly (i.e. glassy). Compare crystalline.

amphoteric: a metal that will react with both acids and alkalis. *Example:* aluminium metal.

anhydrous: lacking water; water has been removed, for example, by heating. Many hydrated salts are crystalline. (Opposite of anhydrous is hydrous or hydrated.) *Example:* copper(II) sulphate can be anhydrous ($CuSO_4$) or hydrated ($CuSO_4 \bullet 5H_2O$).

anion: a negatively charged atom or group of atoms. *Examples:* chloride ion (Cl^-), hydroxide ion (OH^-).

anode: the electrode at which oxidation occurs; the negative terminal of a battery or the positive electrode of an electrolysis cell.

anodising: a process that uses the effect of electrolysis to make a surface corrosion resistant. *Example:* anodised aluminium.

antacid: a common name for any compound that reacts with stomach acid to neutralise it. *Example:* sodium hydrogen carbonate, also known as sodium bicarbonate.

antioxidant: a substance that reacts rapidly with radicals thereby preventing oxidation of some other substance.

anti-bumping granules: small glass or ceramic beads, designed to promote boiling without the development of large gas bubbles.

approximate relative atomic mass: *See:* relative atomic mass.

aqueous: a solution in which the solvent is water. Usually used as 'aqueous solution'. *Example:* aqueous solution of sodium hydroxide ($NaOH(aq)$).

aromatic hydrocarbons: compounds of carbon that have the benzene ring as part of their structure. *Examples:* benzene (C_6H_6), naphthalene ($C_{10}H_8$). They are known as aromatic because of the strong pungent smell given off by benzene.

atmospheric pressure: the pressure exerted by the gases in the air. Units of measurement are kilopascals (kPa), atmospheres (atm), millimetres of mercury (mm Hg) and Torr. Standard atmospheric pressure is 100 kPa, 1atm, 760 mm Hg or 760 Torr.

atom: the smallest particle of an element; a nucleus and its surrounding electrons.

atomic mass: the mass of an atom measured in atomic mass units (amu). An atomic mass unit is equal to one-twelfth of the atom of carbon-12. Atomic mass is now more generally used instead of atomic weight. *Example:* the atomic mass of chlorine is about 35 amu. *See:* atomic weight, relative atomic mass.

atomic number: also known as proton number. The number of electrons or the number of protons in an atom. *Example:* the atomic number of gold is 79 and for carbon it is 4.

atomic structure: the nucleus and the arrangement of electrons around the nucleus of an atom.

atomic weight: a common term used to mean the average molar mass of an element. This is the mass per mole of atoms. *Example:* the atomic weight of chlorine is about 35 g/mol. *See:* atomic mass, mole.

base: a substance that can accept a proton from another substance. *Example:* aqueous ammonia ($NH_3(aq)$). A base can react with an acid in water to form a salt and water.

basic salt: a salt that contains at least one hydroxide ion. The hydroxide ion can then behave as a base in chemical reactions. *Example:* the reaction of hydrochloric acid (HCl) with the base, aluminium hydroxide ($Al(OH)_3$) can form two basic salts, $Al(OH)_2Cl$ and $Al(OH)Cl_2$.

battery: a number of electrochemical cells placed in series.

bauxite: a hydrated impure oxide of aluminium ($Al_2O_3 \bullet xH_2O$, with the amount of water x being variable). It is the main ore used to obtain aluminium metal. The reddish-brown colour of bauxite is mainly caused by the iron oxide impurities it contains.

beehive shelf: an inverted earthenware bowl with a hole in the upper surface and a slot in the rim. Traditionally, the earthenware was brown and looked similar to a beehive, hence its name. A delivery tube passes through the slot and a gas jar is placed over the hole. This provides a convenient way to collect gas over water in a pneumatic trough.

bell jar: a tall glass jar with an open bottom and a wide, stoppered neck that is used in conjunction with a beehive shelf and a pneumatic trough in some experiments involving gases. The name derives from historic versions of the apparatus, which resembled a bell in shape.

blast furnace: a tall furnace charged with a mixture of iron ore, coke and limestone and used for the refining of iron metal. The name comes from the strong blast of air introduced during smelting.

bleach: a substance that removes colour in stains on materials, either by oxidising or reducing the staining compound. *Example:* sulphur dioxide (SO_2).

block: one of the main divisions of the Periodic Table. Blocks are named for the outermost, occupied electron shell of an element. *Example:* The Transition Metals all belong to the d-block.

boiling point: the temperature at which a liquid boils, changing from a liquid to a gas. Boiling points change with atmospheric pressure. *Example:* The boiling point of pure water at standard atmospheric pressure is 100 °C.

boiling tube: A thin glass tube closed at one end and used for chemical tests, etc. The composition and thickness of the glass is such that it cannot sustain very high temperatures and is intended for heating liquids to boiling point. *See:* side-arm boiling tube, test tube.

bond: chemical bonding is either a transfer or sharing of electrons by two or more atoms. There are a number of types of chemical bond, some very strong (such as covalent and ionic bonds), others weak (such as hydrogen bonds). Chemical bonds form because the linked molecule is more stable than the unlinked atoms from which it formed. *Example:* the hydrogen molecule (H_2) is more stable than single atoms of hydrogen, which is why hydrogen gas is always found as molecules of two hydrogen atoms.

Boyle's Law: At constant temperature, and for a given mass of gas, the volume of the gas (V) is inversely proportional to pressure that builds up (P): $P \propto 1/V$.

brine: a solution of salt (sodium chloride, NaCl) in water.

Büchner flask: a thick-walled side-arm flask designed to withstand the changes in pressure that occur when the flask is connected to a suction pump.

Büchner funnel: a special design of plastic or ceramic funnel which has a flat stage on which a filter paper can be placed. It is intended for use under suction with a Büchner funnel.

buffer (solution): a mixture of substances in solution that resists a change in the acidity or alkalinity of the solution when small amounts of an acid or alkali are added.

burette: a long, graduated glass tube with a tap at one end. A burette is used vertically, with the tap lowermost. Its main use is as a reservoir for a chemical during titration.

burn: a combustion reaction in which a flame is produced. A flame occurs where *gases* combust and release heat and light. At least two gases are therefore required if there is to be a flame. *Example:* methane gas (CH_4) burns in oxygen gas (O_2) to produce carbon dioxide (CO_2) and water (H_2O) and give out heat and light.

calorimeter: an insulated container designed to prevent heat gain or loss with the environment and thus allow changes of temperature within reacting chemicals to be measured accurately. It is named after the old unit of heat, the calorie.

capillary: a very small diameter (glass) tube. Capillary tubing has a small enough diameter to allow surface tension effects to retain water within the tube.

capillary action: the tendency for a liquid to be sucked into small spaces, such as between objects and through narrow-pore tubes. The force to do this comes from surface tension.

carbohydrate: a compound containing only carbon, hydrogen and oxygen. Carbohydrates have the formula $C_n(H_2O)_n$, where n is variable. *Example:* glucose ($C_6H_{12}O_6$).

carbonate: a salt of carbonic acid. Carbonate ions have the chemical formula CO_3^{2-}. *Examples:* calcium nitrate $CaCO_3$ and sodium carbonate Na_2CO_3.

catalyst: a substance that speeds up a chemical reaction, but itself remains unaltered at the end of the reaction. *Example:* copper in the reaction of hydrochloric acid with zinc.

catalytic converter: a device incorporated into some exhaust systems. The catalytic converter contains a framework and/or granules with a very large surface area and coated with catalysts that convert the pollutant gases passing over them into harmless products.

cathode: the electrode at which reduction occurs; the positive terminal of a battery or the negative electrode of an electrolysis cell.

cathodic protection: the technique of protecting a metal object by connecting it to a more readily oxidisable metal. The metal object being protected is made into the cathode of a cell. *Example:* iron can be protected by coupling it with magnesium. Iron forms the cathode and magnesium the anode.

cation: a positively charged ion. *Examples:* calcium ion (Ca^{2+}), ammonium ion (NH_4^+).

caustic: a substance that can cause burns if it touches the skin. *Example:* Sodium hydroxide, caustic soda (NaOH).

Celsius scale (°C): a temperature scale on which the freezing point of water is at 0 degrees and the normal boiling point at standard atmospheric pressure is 100 degrees.

cell: a vessel containing two electrodes and an electrolyte that can act as an electrical conductor.

centrifuge: an instrument for spinning small samples very rapidly. The fast spin causes the components of a mixture that have a different density to separate. This has the same effect as filtration.

ceramic: a material based on clay minerals which has been heated so that it has chemically hardened.

chalcogens: the members of Group 6 of the Periodic Table: oxygen, sulphur, selenium and tellurium. The word comes from the Greek meaning 'brass giver', because all these elements are found in copper ores, and copper is the most important metal in making brass.

change of state: a change between two of the three states of matter, solid, liquid and gas. *Example:* when water evaporates it changes from a liquid to a gaseous state.

Charles's Law: The volume (V) of a given mass of gas at constant pressure is directly proportional to its absolute temperature (T): $V \propto T$.

chromatography: A separation technique uses the ability of surfaces to adsorb substances with different strengths. The substances with the least adherence to the surface move faster and leave behind those that adhere more strongly.

coagulation: a term describing the tendency of small particles to stick together in clumps.

coherent: meaning that a substance holds together or sticks together well, and without holes or other defects. *Example:* Aluminium appears unreactive because, as soon as new metal is exposed to air, it forms a very complete oxide coating, which then stops further reaction occurring.

coinage metals: the elements copper, silver and gold, used to make coins.

coke: a solid substance left after the gases have been extracted from coal.

colloid: a mixture of ultramicroscopic particles dispersed uniformly through a second substance to form a suspension which may be almost like a solution or may set to a jelly (gel). The word comes from the Greek for glue.

colorimeter: an instrument for measuring the light-absorbing power of a substance. The absorption gives an accurate indication of the concentration of some coloured solutions.

combustion: a reaction in which an element or compound is oxidised to release energy. Some combustion reactions are slow, such as the combustion of the sugar we eat to provide our energy. If the combustion results in a flame, it is called burning. A flame occurs where *gases* combust and release heat and light. At least two gases are therefore required if there is to be a flame. *Example:* the combustion or burning of methane gas (CH_4) in oxygen gas (O_2) produces carbon dioxide (CO_2) and water (H_2O) and gives out heat and light. Some combustion reactions produce light and heat but do not produce flames. *Example:* the combustion of carbon in oxygen produces an intense red–white light but no flame.

combustion spoon: also known as a deflagrating spoon, it consists of a long metal handle with a small cup at the end. Its purpose is to allow the safe introduction of a (usually heated) substance into a gas jar filled with gas, when the reaction is likely to be vigorous. *Example:* the introduction of a heated sodium pellet into a gas jar containing chlorine.

compound: a chemical consisting of two or more elements chemically bonded together. *Example:* Calcium atoms can combine with carbon atoms and oxygen atoms to make calcium carbonate ($CaCO_3$), a compound of all three atoms.

condensation: the formation of a liquid from a gas. This is a change of state, also called a phase change.

condensation nuclei: microscopic particles of dust, salt and other materials suspended in the air, that attract water molecules. The usual result is the formation of water droplets.

condensation polymer: a polymer formed by a chain of reactions in which a water molecule is eliminated as every link of the polymer is formed. *Examples:* polyesters, proteins, nylon.

conduction: (i) the exchange of heat (heat conduction) by contact with another object, or (ii) allowing the flow of electrons (electrical conduction).

conductivity: the ability of a substance to conduct. The conductivity of a solution depends on there being suitable free ions in the solution. A conducting solution is called an electrolyte. *Example:* dilute sulphuric acid.

convection: the exchange of heat energy with the surroundings produced by the flow of a fluid due to being heated or cooled.

corrosion: the oxidation of a metal. Corrosion is often regarded as unwanted and is more generally used to refer to the *slow* decay of a metal resulting from contact with gases and liquids in the environment. *Example:* Rust is the corrosion of iron.

corrosive: causing corrosion. *Example:* Sodium hydroxide ($NaOH$).

covalent bond: this is the most common form of strong chemical bonding and occurs when two atoms *share* electrons. *Example:* oxygen (O_2)

cracking: breaking down complex molecules into simpler compounds, as in oil refining.

crucible: a small bowl with a lip, made of heat-resistant white glazed ceramic. It is used for heating substances using a Bunsen flame.

crude oil: a chemical mixture of petroleum liquids. Crude oil forms the raw material for an oil refinery.

crystal: a substance that has grown freely so that it can develop external faces. Compare crystalline, where the atoms are not free to form individual crystals and amorphous, where the atoms are arranged irregularly.

crystalline: a solid in which the atoms, ions or molecules are organised into an orderly pattern without distinct crystal faces. *Examples:* copper(II) sulphate, sodium chloride. Compare amorphous.

crystallisation: the process in which a solute comes out of solution slowly and forms crystals. *See:* water of crystallisation.

crystal systems: seven patterns or systems into which all crystals can be grouped: cubic, hexagonal, rhombohedral, tetragonal, orthorhombic, monoclinic and triclinic.

cubic crystal system: groupings of crystals that look like cubes.

current: an electric current is produced by a flow of electrons through a conducting solid or ions through a conducting liquid. The rate of supply of this charge is measured in amperes (A).

decay (radioactive decay): the way that a radioactive element changes into another element due to loss of mass through radiation. *Example:* uranium 238 decays with the loss of an alpha particle to form thorium 234.

decomposition: the break down of a substance (for example, by heat or with the aid of a catalyst) into simpler components. In such a chemical reaction only one substance is involved. *Example:* hydrogen peroxide ($H_2O_2(aq)$) into oxygen ($O_2(g)$) and water ($H_2O(l)$).

decrepitation: when, as part of the decomposition of a substance, cracking sounds are also produced. *Example:* heating of lead nitrate ($Pb(NO_3)_2$).

dehydration: the removal of water from a substance by heating it, placing it in a dry atmosphere or using a drying (dehydrating) reagent such as concentrated sulphuric acid.

density: the mass per unit volume (e.g. g/cc).

desalinisation: the removal of all the salts from sea water, by reverse osmosis or heating the water and collecting the distillate. It is a very energy-intensive process.

desiccant: a substance that absorbs water vapour from the air. *Example:* silica gel.

desiccator: a glass bowl and lid containing a shelf. The apparatus is designed to store materials in dry air. A desiccant is placed below the shelf and the substance to be dried is placed on the shelf. The lid makes a gas-tight joint with the bowl.

destructive distillation: the heating of a material so that it decomposes entirely to release all of its volatile components. Destructive distillation is also known as pyrolysis.

detergent: a chemical based on petroleum that removes dirt.

Devarda's alloy: zinc with a trace of copper, which acts as a catalyst for reactions with the zinc.

diaphragm: a semipermeable membrane – a kind of ultrafine mesh filter – that allows only small ions to pass through. It is used in the electrolysis of brine.

diffusion: the slow mixing of one substance with another until the two substances are evenly mixed. Mixing occurs because of differences in concentration within the mixture. Diffusion works rapidly with gases, very slowly with liquids.

diffusion combustion: the form of combustion that occurs when two gases only begin to mix during ignition. As a result the flame is hollow and yellow in colour. *Example:* a candle flame.

dilute acid: an acid whose concentration has been reduced in a large proportion of water.

disinfectant: a chemical that kills bacteria and other microorganisms.

displacement reaction: a reaction that occurs because metals differ in their reactivity. If a more reactive metal is placed in a solution of a less reactive metal compound, a reaction occurs in which the more reactive metal displaces the metal ions in the solution. *Example:* when zinc metal is introduced into a solution of copper(II) sulphate (which thus contains copper ions), zinc goes into solution as zinc ions, while copper is displaced from the solution and forced to precipitate as metallic copper.

dissociate: to break bonds apart. In the case of acids, it means to break up, forming hydrogen ions. This is an example of ionisation. Strong acids dissociate completely. Weak acids are not completely ionised, and a solution of a weak acid has a relatively low concentration of hydrogen ions.

dissolve: to break down a substance in a solution without causing a reaction.

distillation: the process of separating mixtures by condensing the vapours through cooling.

distilled water: distilled water is nearly pure water and is produced by distillation of tap water. Distilled water is used in the laboratory in preference to tap water because the distillation process removes many of the impurities in tap water that may influence the chemical reactions for which the water is used.

Dreschel bottle: a tall bottle with a special stopper, designed to allow a gas to pass through a liquid. The stopper contains both inlet and outlet tubes. One tube extends below the surface of the liquid so that the gas has to pass through the liquid before it can escape to the outlet tube.

dropper funnel: a special funnel with a tap to allow the controlled release of a liquid. Also known as a dropping funnel or tap funnel.

drying agent: *See:* dehydrating agent.

dye: a coloured substance that will stick to another substance so that both appear coloured.

effervesce: to give off bubbles of gas.

effloresce: to lose water and turn to a fine powder on exposure to the air. *Example:* Sodium carbonate on the rim of a reagent bottle stopper.

electrical conductivity: *See:* conductivity

electrical potential: the energy produced by an electrochemical cell and measured by the voltage or electromotive force (emf). *See:* potential difference, electromotive force.

electrochemical cell: a cell consisting of two electrodes and an electrolyte. It can be set up to generate an electric current (usually known as a galvanic cell, an example of which is a battery), or an electric current can be passed through it to produce a chemical reaction (in which case it is called an electrolytic cell and can be used to refine metals or for electroplating).

electrochemical series: the arrangement of substances that are either oxidising or reducing agents in order of strength as a reagent, for example, with the strong oxidising agents at the top of the list and the strong reducing agents at the bottom.

electrode: a conductor that forms one terminal of a cell.

electrolysis: an electrical–chemical process that uses an electric current to cause the break-up of a compound and the movement of metal ions in a solution. The process happens in many natural situations (as for example in rusting) and is also commonly used

in industry for purifying (refining) metals or for plating metal objects with a fine, even metal coating.

electrolyte: an ionic solution that conducts electricity.

electrolytic cell: *See:* electrochemical cell.

electromotive force (emf): the force set up in an electric circuit by a potential difference.

electron: a tiny, negatively charged particle that is part of an atom. The flow of electrons through a solid material such as a wire produces an electric current.

electron configuration: the pattern in which electrons are arranged in shells around the nucleus of an atom. *Example:* chlorine has the configuration 2, 8, 7.

electroplating: depositing a thin layer of a metal on to the surface of another substance using electrolysis.

element: a substance that cannot be decomposed into simpler substance by chemical means. *Examples:* calcium, iron, gold.

emulsion: tiny droplets of one substance dispersed in another. One common oil in water emulsion is called milk. Because the tiny droplets tend to come together, another stabilising substance is often needed. Soaps and detergents are such agents, wrapping the particles of grease and oil in a stable coat. Photographic film is an example of a solid emulsion.

endothermic reaction: a reaction that takes in heat. *Example:* when ammonium chloride is dissolved in water.

end point: the stage in a titration when the reaction between the titrant (added from a burette) and the titrate (in the flask) is complete. The end point is normally recognised by use of an indicator which has been added to

the titrate. In an acid–base reaction this is also called the neutralisation point.

enzyme: biological catalysts in the form of proteins in the body that speed up chemical reactions. Every living cell contains hundreds of enzymes that help the processes of life continue.

ester: organic compounds formed by the reaction of an alcohol with an acid and which often have a fruity taste. *Example:* ethyl acetate ($CH_3COOC_2H_5$).

evaporation: the change of state of a liquid to a gas. Evaporation happens below the boiling point and is used as a method of separating the materials in a solution.

excess, to: if a reactant has been added to another reactant in excess, it has exceeded the amount required to complete the reaction.

exothermic reaction: a reaction that gives out substantial amounts of heat. *Example:* sucrose and concentrated sulphuric acid.

explosive: a substance which, when a shock is applied to it, decomposes very rapidly, releasing a very large amount of heat and creating a large volume of gases as a shock wave.

fats: semisolid, energy-rich compounds derived from plants or animals, made of carbon, hydrogen and oxygen. These are examples of esters.

ferment: to break down a substance by microorganisms in the absence of oxygen. *Example:* fermentation of sugar to ethanol during the production of alcoholic drinks.

filtrate: the liquid that has passed through a filter.

filtration: the separation of a liquid from a solid using a membrane with small holes (i.e. a filter paper).

flame: a mixture of gases undergoing burning. A solid or liquid must produce a gas before it can react with oxygen and burn with a flame.

flammable (also inflammable): able to burn (in air). *Opposite:* non-flammable.

flocculation: the grouping together of small particles in a suspension to form particles large enough to settle out as a precipitate. Flocculation is usually caused by the presence of a flocculating agent. *Example:* calcium ions are the flocculating agent for suspended clay particles.

fluid: able to flow; either a liquid or a gas.

fluorescent: a substance that gives out visible light when struck by invisible waves, such as ultraviolet rays.

flux: a material used to make it easier for a liquid to flow. A flux dissolves metal oxides and so prevents a metal from oxidising while being heated.

foam: a substance that is sufficiently gelatinous to be able to contain bubbles of gas. The gas bulks up the substance, making it behave as though it were semirigid.

fossil fuels: hydrocarbon compounds that have been formed from buried plant and animal remains. High pressures and temperatures lasting over millions of years are required. *Examples:* The fossil fuels are coal, oil and natural gas.

fraction: a group of similar components of a mixture. *Example:* In the petroleum industry the light fractions of crude oil are those with the smallest molecules, while the medium and heavy fractions have larger molecules.

fractional distillation: the separation of the components of a liquid mixture by heating them to their boiling points.

fractionating column: a glass column designed to allow different fractions to be separated when they boil. In industry, it may be called a fractionating tower.

free radical: a very reactive atom or group with a 'spare' electron. *Example:* methyl, $CH_3\bullet$.

freezing point: the temperature at which a substance undergoes a phase change from a liquid to a solid. It is the same temperature as the melting point.

fuel: a concentrated form of chemical energy. The main sources of fuels (called fossil fuels because they were formed by geological processes) are coal, crude oil and natural gas.

fuel rods: the rods of uranium or other radioactive material used as a fuel in nuclear power stations.

fume chamber or fume cupboard: a special laboratory chamber fitted with a protective glass shield and containing a powerful extraction fan to remove toxic fumes.

fuming: an unstable liquid that gives off a gas. Very concentrated acid solutions are often fuming solutions. *Example:* fuming nitric acid.

galvanising: applying a thin zinc coating to protect another metal.

gamma rays: waves of radiation produced as the nucleus of a radioactive element rearranges itself into a tighter cluster of protons and neutrons. Gamma rays carry enough energy to damage living cells.

gangue: the unwanted material in an ore.

gas/gaseous phase: a form of matter in which the molecules form no definite shape and are free to move about to uniformly fill any vessel they are put in. A gas can easily be compressed into a much smaller volume.

gas syringe: a glass syringe with a graduated cylinder designed to collect and measure small amounts of gases produced during an experiment.

gelatinous precipitate: a precipitate that has a jelly-like appearance. *Example:* iron (III) hydroxide. Because a gelatinous precipitate is mostly water, it is of a similar density to water and will float or lie suspended in the liquid. *See:* granular precipitate.

glass: a transparent silicate without any crystal growth. It has a glassy lustre and breaks with a curved fracture. Note that some minerals have all these features and are therefore natural glasses. Household glass is a synthetic silicate.

glucose: the most common of the natural sugars ($C_6H_{12}O_6$). It occurs as the polymer known as cellulose, the fibre in plants. Starch is also a form of glucose.

granular precipitate: a precipitate that has a grain-like appearance. *Example:* lead(II) hydroxide. *See:* gelatinous precipitate.

gravimetric analysis: a quantitative form of analysis in which the mass (weight) of the reactants and products is measured.

group: a vertical column in the Periodic Table. There are eight groups in the table. Their numbers correspond to the number of electrons in the outer shell of the atoms in the group. *Example:* Group 1: member, sodium.

Greenhouse Effect: an increase in the global air temperature as a result of heat released from burning fossil fuels being absorbed by carbon dioxide in the atmosphere.

Greenhouse gas: any of various the gases that contribute to the Greenhouse Effect. *Example:* carbon dioxide.

half-life: the time it takes for the radiation coming from a sample of a radioactive element to decrease by half.

halide: a salt of one of the halogens.

halogen: one of a group of elements including chlorine, bromine, iodine and fluorine in Group 7 of the Periodic Table.

heat: the energy that is transferred when a substance is at a different temperature to that of its surroundings. *See:* endothermic and exothermic reactions.

heat capacity: the ratio of the heat supplied to a substance, compared with the rise in temperature that is produced.

heat of combustion: the amount of heat given off by a mole of a substance during combustion. This heat is a property of the substance and is the same no matter what kind of combustion is involved. *Example:* heat of combustion of carbon is 94.05 kcal (x 4.18 = 393.1 kJ).

hydrate: a solid compound in crystalline form that contains water molecules. Hydrates commonly form when a solution of a soluble salt is evaporated. The water that forms part of a hydrate crystal is known as the 'water of crystallisation'. It can usually be removed by heating, leaving an anhydrous salt.

hydration: the process of absorption of water by a substance. In some cases hydration makes the substance change colour; in many other cases there is no colour change, simply a change in volume. *Example:* dark blue hydrated copper(II) sulphate ($CuSO_4 \cdot 5H_2O$) can be heated to produce white anhydrous copper(II) sulphate ($CuSO_4$).

hydride: a compound containing just hydrogen and another element, most often a metal.

Examples: water (H_2O), methane (CH_4) and phosphine (PH_3).

hydrous: hydrated with water. *See:* anhydrous.

hydrocarbon: a compound in which only hydrogen and carbon atoms are present. Most fuels are hydrocarbons, as is the simple plastic, polyethene. *Example:* methane CH_4.

hydrogen bond: a type of attractive force that holds one molecule to another. It is one of the weaker forms of intermolecular attractive force. *Example:* hydrogen bonds occur in water.

ignition temperature: the temperature at which a substance begins to burn.

immiscible: will not mix with another substance. e.g., oil and water.

incandescent: glowing or shining with heat. *Example:* tungsten filament in an incandescent light bulb.

incomplete combustion: combustion in which only some of the reactant or reactants combust, or the products are not those that would be obtained if all the reactions went to completion. It is uncommon for combustion to be complete and incomplete combustion is more frequent. *Example:* incomplete combustion of carbon in oxygen produces carbon monoxide and not carbon dioxide.

indicator (acid–base indicator): a substance or mixture of substances used to test the acidity or alkalinity of a substance. An indicator changes colour depending on the acidity of the solution being tested. Many indicators are complicated organic substances. Some indicators used in the laboratory include Universal Indicator, litmus, phenolphthalein, methyl orange and bromothymol. *See:* Universal Indicator.

induction period: the time taken for a reaction to reach ignition temperature. During this period, no apparent reaction occurs, then the materials appear to undergo spontaneous combustion.

inert: unreactive.

inhibitor: a substance that prevents a reaction from occurring.

inorganic substance: a substance that does not contain carbon and hydrogen. *Examples:* NaCl, $CaCO_3$.

insoluble: a substance that will not dissolve.

ion: an atom, or group of atoms, that has gained or lost one or more electrons and so developed an electrical charge. Ions behave differently from electrically neutral atoms and molecules. They can move in an electric field, and they can also bind strongly to solvent molecules such as water. Positively charged ions are called cations; negatively charged ions are called anions. Ions can carry an electrical current through solutions.

ionic bond: the form of bonding that occurs between two ions when the ions have opposite charges. *Example:* sodium cations bond with chloride anions to form common salt (NaCl) when a salty solution is evaporated. Ionic bonds are strong bonds except in the presence of a solvent. *See:* bond.

ionic compound: a compound that consists of ions. *Example:* NaCl.

ionise: to break up neutral molecules into oppositely charged ions or to convert atoms into ions by the loss of electrons.

ionisation: a process that creates ions.

isotope: an atom that has the same number of protons in its nucleus, but which has a different mass. *Example:* carbon 12 and carbon 14.

Kipp's apparatus: a piece of glassware consisting of three

chambers, designed to provide a continuous and regulated production of gas by bringing the reactants into contact in a controlled way.

lanthanide series or lanthanide metals: a series of 15 similar metallic elements between lanthanum and lutetium. They are transition metals and also also called rare earths.

latent heat: the amount of heat that is absorbed or released during the process of changing state between gas, liquid and solid. For example, heat is absorbed when a substance melts and it is released again when the substance solidifies.

lattice: a regular arrangement of atoms, ions or molecules in a crystalline solid.

leaching: the extraction of a substance by percolating a solvent through a material. *Example:* when water flows through an ore, some of the heavy metals in it may be leached out causing environmental pollution.

Liebig condenser: a piece of glassware consisting of a sloping water-cooled tube. The design allows a volatile material to be condensed and collected.

liquefaction: to make something liquid.

liquid/liquid phase: a form of matter that has a fixed volume but no fixed shape.

lime (quicklime): calcium oxide (CaO). A white, caustic solid, manufactured by heating limestone and used for making mortar, fertiliser or bleach.

limewater: an aqueous solution of calcium hydroxide, used especially to detect the presence of carbon dioxide.

litmus: an indicator obtained from lichens. Used as a solution or impregnated into paper (litmus paper), which is dampened before use. Litmus turns red under acid conditions and purple in alkaline conditions. Litmus is a crude indicator when compared with Universal Indicator.

load (electronics): an impedance or circuit that receives or develops the output of a cell or other power supply.

lustre: the shininess of a substance.

malleable: able to be pressed or hammered into shape.

manometer: a device for measuring gas pressure. A simple manometer is made by partly filling a U-shaped rubber tube with water and connecting one end to the source of gas whose pressure is to be measured. The pressure is always relative to atmospheric pressure.

mass: the amount of matter in an object. In everyday use the word weight is often used (somewhat incorrectly) to mean mass.

matter: anything that has mass and takes up space.

melting point: the temperature at which a substance changes state from a solid phase to a liquid phase. It is the same as freezing point.

membrane: a thin, flexible sheet. A semipermeable membrane has microscopic holes of a size that will selectively allow some ions and molecules to pass through but hold others back. It thus acts as a kind of filter. *Example:* a membrane used for osmosis.

meniscus: the curved surface of a liquid that forms in a small bore or capillary tube. The meniscus is convex (bulges upwards) for mercury and is concave (sags downwards) for water.

metal: a class of elements that is a good conductor of electricity and heat, has a metallic lustre, is malleable and ductile, forms cations and has oxides that are bases. Metals are formed as cations

held together by a sea of electrons. A metal may also be an alloy of these elements. *Example:* sodium, calcium, gold. *See:* alloy, metalloid, non-metal.

metallic bonding: cations reside in a 'sea' of mobile electrons. It allows metals to be good conductors and means that they are not brittle. *See:* bonding.

metallic lustre: *See:* lustre.

metalloid: a class of elements intermediate in properties between metals and non-metals. Metalloids are also called semi-metals or semiconductors. *Example:* silicon, germanium, antimony. *See:* metal, non-metal, semiconductor.

micronutrient: an element that the body requires in small amounts. Another term is trace element.

mineral: a solid substance made of just one element or compound. *Example:* calcite is a mineral because it consists only of calcium carbonate; halite is a mineral because it contains only sodium chloride.

mineral acid: an acid that does not contain carbon and which attacks minerals. Hydrochloric, sulphuric and nitric acids are the main mineral acids.

miscible: capable of being mixed.

mixing combustion: the form of combustion that occurs when two gases thoroughly mix before they ignite and so produce almost complete combustion. *Example:* when a Bunsen flame is blue.

mixture: a material that can be separated into two or more substances using physical means. *Example:* a mixture of copper(II) sulphate and cadmium sulphide can be separated by filtration.

molar mass: the mass per mole of atoms of an element. It has the same value and uses the same units as atomic weight. *Example:* molar mass of chlorine is 35.45 g/mol. *See:* atomic weight.

mole: 1 mole is the amount of a substance which contains Avagadro's number (6 x 10^{23}) of particles. *Example:* 1 mole of carbon-12 weighs exactly 12 g.

molecular mass: *See:* molar mass.

molecular weight: *See:* molar mass.

molecule: a group of two or more atoms held together by chemical bonds. *Example:* O_2.

monoclinic system: a grouping of crystals that look like double-ended chisel blades.

monomer: a small molecule and building block for larger chain molecules or polymers ('mono' means one, 'mer' means part). *Examples:* tetrafluoroethene for teflon, ethene for polyethene.

native element: an element that occurs in an uncombined state. *Examples:* sulphur, gold.

native metal: a pure form of a metal, not combined as a compound. Native metal is more common in poorly reactive elements than in those that are very reactive. *Examples:* copper, gold.

net ionic reaction: the overall, or net, change that occurs in a reaction, seen in terms of ions.

neutralisation: the reaction of acids and bases to produce a salt and water. The reaction causes hydrogen from the acid and hydroxide from the base to be changed to water. *Example:* hydrochloric acid reacts with, and neutralises, sodium hydroxide to form the salt sodium chloride (common salt) and water. The term is more generally used for any reaction in which the pH changes toward 7.0, which is the pH of a neutral solution. *See:* pH.

neutralisation point: *See:* end point.

neutron: a particle inside the nucleus of an atom that is neutral and has no charge.

newton (N): the unit of force required to give one kilogram an acceleration of one metre per second every second (1 ms^{-2}).

nitrate: a compound that includes nitrogen and oxygen and contains more oxygen than a nitrite. Nitrate ions have the chemical formula NO_3^-. *Examples:* sodium nitrate $NaNO_3$ and lead nitrate $Pb(NO_3)_2$.

nitrite: a compound that includes nitrogen and oxygen and contains less oxygen than a nitrate. Nitrite ions have the chemical formula NO_2^-. *Example:* sodium nitrite $NaNO_2$.

noble gases: the members of Group 8 of the Periodic Table: helium, neon, argon, krypton, xenon, radon. These gases are almost entirely unreactive.

noble metals: silver, gold, platinum and mercury. These are the least reactive metals.

non-combustible: a substance that will not combust or burn. *Example:* carbon dioxide.

non-metal: a brittle substance that does not conduct electricity. *Examples:* sulphur, phosphorus, all gases. *See:* metal, metalloid.

normal salt: salts that do not contain a hydroxide (OH$^-$) ion, which would make them basic salts, or a hydrogen ion, which would make them acid salts. *Example:* sodium chloride (NaCl).

nucleus: the small, positively charged particle at the centre of an atom. The nucleus is responsible for most of the mass of an atom.

opaque: a substance that will not transmit light so that it is impossible to see through it. Most solids are opaque.

ore: a rock containing enough of a useful substance to make mining it worthwhile. *Example:* bauxite, aluminium ore.

organic acid: an acid containing carbon and hydrogen. *Example:* methanoic (formic) acid (HCOOH).

organic chemistry: the study of organic compounds.

organic compound (organic substance; organic material): a compound (or substance) that contains carbon and usually hydrogen. (The carbonates are usually excluded.) *Examples:* methane (CH_4), chloromethane (CH_3Cl), ethene (C_2H_4), ethanol (C_2H_5OH), ethanoic acid (C_2H_3OOH), etc.

organic solvent: an organic substance that will dissolve other substances. *Example:* carbon tetrachloride (CCl_4).

osmosis: a process whereby molecules of a liquid solvent move through a semipermeable membrane from a region of low concentration of a solute to a region with a high concentration of a solute.

oxidation–reduction reaction (redox reaction): reaction in which oxidation and reduction occurs; a reaction in which electrons are transferred. *Example:* copper and oxygen react to produce copper(II) oxide. The copper is oxidised, and oxygen is reduced.

oxidation: combination with oxygen or a reaction in which an atom, ion or molecule loses electrons to an oxidising agent. (Note that an oxidising agent does not have to contain oxygen.) The opposite of oxidation is reduction. *See:* reduction.

oxidation number (oxidation state): the effective charge on an atom in a compound. An increase in oxidation number corresponds to oxidation, and a decrease to reduction. Shown in Roman numerals. *Example:* manganate(IV).

oxidation state: *See:* oxidation number.

oxide: a compound that includes oxygen and one other element. *Example:* copper oxide (CuO).

oxidise: to combine with or gain oxygen or to react such that an atom, ion or molecule loses electrons to an oxidising agent.

oxidising agent: a substance that removes electrons from another substance being oxidised (and therefore is itself reduced) in a redox reaction. *Example:* chlorine (Cl_2).

ozone: a form of oxygen whose molecules contain three atoms of oxygen. Ozone is regarded as a beneficial gas when high in the atmosphere because it blocks ultraviolet rays. It is a harmful gas when breathed in, so low level ozone which is produced as part of city smog is regarded as a form of pollution. The ozone layer is the uppermost part of the stratosphere.

partial pressure: the pressure a gas in a mixture would exert if it alone occupied a flask. *Example:* oxygen makes up about a fifth of the atmosphere. Its partial pressure is therefore about a fifth of normal atmospheric pressure.

pascal: the unit of pressure, equal to one newton per square metre of surface. *See:* newton.

patina: a surface coating that develops on metals and protects them from further corrosion. *Example:* the green coating of copper carbonate that forms on copper statues.

percolate: to move slowly through the pores of a rock.

period: a row in the Periodic Table.

Periodic Table: a chart organising elements by atomic number and chemical properties into groups and periods.

pestle and mortar: a pestle is a ceramic rod with a rounded end, a mortar is a ceramic dish. Pestle and mortar are used together to pound or grind solids into fine powders.

Petri dish: a shallow glass or plastic dish with a lid.

petroleum: a natural mixture of a range of gases, liquids and solids derived from the decomposed remains of plants and animals.

pH: a measure of the hydrogen ion concentration in a liquid. Neutral is pH 7.0; numbers greater than this are alkaline; smaller numbers are acidic. *See:* neutralisation, acid, base.

pH meter: a device that accurately measures the pH of a solution. A pH meter is a voltmeter that measures the electric potential difference between two electrodes (which are attached to the meter through a probe) when they are submerged in a solution. The readings are shown on a dial or digital display.

phase: a particular state of matter. A substance may exist as a solid, liquid or gas and may change between these phases with addition or removal of energy. *Examples:* ice, liquid and vapour are the three phases of water. Ice undergoes a phase change to water when heat energy is added.

phosphor: any material that glows when energised by ultraviolet or electron beams, such as in fluorescent tubes and cathode ray tubes. Phosphors, such as phosphorus, emit light after the source of excitation is cut off. This is why they glow in the dark. By contrast, fluorescers, such as fluorite, only emit light while they are being excited by ultraviolet light or an electron beam.

photochemical smog: photochemical reactions are caused by the energy of sunlight. Photochemical smog is a mixture of tiny particles and a brown haze caused by the reaction of colourless nitric oxide from vehicle exhausts and oxygen of the air to form brown nitrogen dioxide.

photon: a parcel of light energy.

photosynthesis: the process by which plants use the energy of the Sun to make the compounds they need for life. In photosynthesis, six molecules of carbon dioxide from the air combine with six molecules of water, forming one molecule of glucose (sugar) and releasing six molecules of oxygen back into the atmosphere.

pipe-clay triangle: a device made from three small pieces of ceramic tube which are wired together in the shape of a triangle. Pipe-clay triangles are used to support round-bottomed dishes when they are heated in a Bunsen flame.

pipette: a log, slender, glass tube used, in conjunction with a pipette filler, to draw up and then transfer accurately measured amounts of liquid.

plastic: (material) a carbon-based substance consisting of long chains (polymers) of simple molecules. The word plastic is commonly restricted to synthetic polymers. *Examples:* polyvinyl chloride, nylon: **(property)** a material is plastic if it can be made to change shape easily. Plastic materials will remain in the new shape. (Compare with elastic, a property whereby a material goes back to its original shape.)

pneumatic trough: a shallow water-filled glass dish used to house a beehive shelf and a gas jar as part of the apparatus for collecting a gas over water.

polar solvent: a solvent in which the atoms have partial electric charges. *Example:* water.

polymer: a compound that is made of long chains by combining molecules (called monomers) as repeating units. ('Poly' means many, 'mer' means part.) *Examples:* polytetrafluoroethene or Teflon from tetrafluoroethene, Terylene from terephthalic acid and ethane-1,2-diol (ethylene glycol).

polymerisation: a chemical reaction in which large numbers of similar molecules arrange themselves into large molecules, usually long chains. This process usually happens when there is a suitable catalyst present. *Example:* ethene gas reacts to form polyethene in the presence of certain catalysts.

polymorphism: (meaning many shapes) the tendency of some materials to have more than one solid form. *Example:* carbon as diamond, graphite and buckminsterfullerene.

porous: a material containing many small holes or cracks. Quite often the pores are connected, and liquids, such as water or oil, can move through them.

potential difference: a measure of the work that must be done to move an electric charge from one point to the other in a circuit. Potential difference is measured in volts, V. *See:* electrical potential.

precious metal: silver, gold, platinum, iridium and palladium. Each is prized for its rarity.

precipitate: a solid substance formed as a result of a chemical reaction between two liquids or gases. *Example:* iron(III) hydroxide is precipitated when sodium hydroxide solution is added to iron(III) chloride. *See:* gelatinous precipitate, granular precipitate.

preservative: a substance that prevents the natural organic decay processes from occurring. Many substances can be used safely for this purpose, including sulphites and nitrogen gas.

pressure: the force per unit area measured in pascals. *See:* pascal, atmospheric pressure.

product: a substance produced by a chemical reaction. *Example:* when the reactants copper and oxygen react, they produce the product, copper oxide.

proton: a positively charged particle in the nucleus of an atom that balances out the charge of the surrounding electrons.

proton number: this is the modern expression for atomic number. *See:* atomic number.

purify: to remove all impurities from a mixture, perhaps by precipitation, or filtration.

pyrolysis: chemical decomposition brought about by heat. *Example:* decomposition of lead nitrate. *See:* destructive distillation.

pyrometallurgy: refining a metal from its ore using heat. A blast furnace or smelter is the main equipment used.

quantitative: measurement of the amounts of constituents of a substance, for example by mass or volume. *See:* gravimetric analysis, volumetric analysis.

radiation: the exchange of energy with the surroundings through the transmission of waves or particles of energy. Radiation is a form of energy transfer that can happen through space; no intervening medium is required (as would be the case for conduction and convection).

radical: an atom, molecule, or ion with at least one unpaired electron. *Example:* nitrogen monoxide (NO).

radioactive: emitting radiation or particles from the nucleus of its atoms.

radioactive decay: a change in a radioactive element due to loss of mass through radiation. For example, uranium decays (changes) to lead.

reactant: a starting material that takes part in, and undergoes, change during a chemical reaction. *Example:* hydrochloric acid and calcium carbonate are reactants; the reaction produces the products calcium chloride, carbon dioxide and water.

reaction: the recombination of two substances using parts of each substance to produce new substances. *Example:* the reactants sodium chloride and sulphuric acid react and recombine to form the products sodium sulphate, chlorine and water.

reactivity: the tendency of a substance to react with other substances. The term is most widely used in comparing the reactivity of metals. Metals are arranged in a reactivity series.

reactivity series: the series of metals organised in order of their reactivity, with the most reactive metals, such as sodium, at the top and the least react metals, such as gold, at the bottom. Hydrogen is usually included in the series for comparative purposes.

reagent: a commonly available substance (reactant) used to create a reaction. Reagents are the chemicals normally kept on chemistry laboratory benches. Many substances called reagents are most commonly used for test purposes.

redox reaction (oxidation–reduction reaction): a reaction that involves oxidation and reduction; a reactions in which electrons are transferred. *See:* oxidation–reduction.

reducing agent: a substance that gives electrons to another substance being reduced (and therefore itself being oxidised) in a redox reaction. *Example:* hydrogen sulphide (H_2S).

reduction: the removal of oxygen from, or the addition of hydrogen to, a compound. Also a reaction in which an atom, ion or molecule gains electrons from a reducing agent. (The opposite of reduction is oxidation.)

reduction tube: a boiling tube with a small hole near the closed end. The tube is mounted horizontally, a sample is placed in the tube and a reducing gas, such as carbon monoxide, is passed through the tube. The oxidised gas escapes through the small hole.

refining: separating a mixture into the simpler substances of which it is made.

reflux distillation system: a form of distillation using a Liebig condenser placed vertically, so that all the vapours created during boiling are condensed back into the liquid, rather than escaping. In this way, the concentration of all the reactants remains constant.

relative atomic mass: in the past a measure of the mass of an atom on a scale relative to the mass of an atom of hydrogen, where hydrogen is 1. Nowadays a measure of the mass of an atom relative to the mass of one twelfth of an atom of carbon-12. If the relative atomic mass is given as a rounded figure, it is called an approximate relative atomic mass. *Examples:* chlorine 35, calcium 40, gold 197. *See:* atomic mass, atomic weight.

reversible reaction: a reaction in which the products can be transformed back into their original chemical form. *Example:* heated iron reacts with steam to produce iron oxide and hydrogen. If the hydrogen is passed over this heated oxide, it forms iron and steam. $3Fe + 4H_2O \rightleftharpoons Fe_3O_4 + 4H_2$.

roast: heating a substance for a long time at a high temperature, as in a furnace.

rust: the product of the corrosion of iron and steel in the presence of air and water.

salt: a compound, often involving a metal, that is the reaction product of an acid and a base, or of two elements. (Note 'salt' is also the common word for sodium chloride, common salt or table salt.) *Example:* sodium chloride (NaCl) and potassium sulphate (K_2SO_4) *See:* acid salt, basic salt, normal salt.

salt bridge: a permeable material soaked in a salt solution that allows ions to be transferred from one container to another. The salt solution remains unchanged during this transfer. *Example:* sodium sulphate used as a salt bridge in a galvanic cell.

saponification: a reaction between a fat and a base that produces a soap.

saturated: a state in which a liquid can hold no more of a substance. If any more of the substance is added, it will not dissolve.

saturated hydrocarbon: a hydrocarbon in which the carbon atoms are held with single bonds. *Example:* ethane (C_2H_6).

saturated solution: a solution that holds the maximum possible amount of dissolved material. When saturated, the rate of dissolving solid and that of recrystallisation solid are the same, and a condition of equilibrium is reached. The amount of material in solution varies with the temperature; cold solutions can hold less dissolved solid material than hot solutions. Gases are more soluble in cold liquids than in hot liquids.

sediment: material that settles out at the bottom of a liquid when it is still. A precipitate is one form of sediment.

semiconductor: a material of intermediate conductivity. Semiconductor devices often use silicon when they are made as part of diodes, transistors or integrated circuits. Elements intermediate between metals and non-metals are also sometimes called semiconductors. *Example:* germanium oxide, germanium. *See:* metalloid.

semipermeable membrane: a thin material that acts as a fine sieve or filter, allowing small molecules to pass, but holding large molecules back.

separating column: used in chromatography. A tall glass tube containing a porous disc near the base and filled with a substance (for example, aluminium oxide, which is known as a stationary phase) that can adsorb materials on its surface. When a mixture is passed through the column, fractions are retarded by differing amounts, so that each fraction is washed through the column in sequence.

separating funnel: a pear-shaped, glassware funnel designed to permit the separation of immiscible liquids by simply pouring off the more dense liquid while leaving the less dense liquid in the funnel.

series circuit: an electrical circuit in which all of the components are joined end to end in a line.

shell: the term used to describe the imaginary ball-shaped surface outside the nucleus of an atom that would be formed by a set of electrons of similar energy. The outermost shell is known as the valence shell. *Example:* neon has shells containing 2 and 8 electrons.

side-arm boiling tube: a boiling tube with an integral glass pipe near its open end. The side arm is normally used for the entry or exit of a gas.

simple distillation: the distillation of a substance when only one volatile fraction is to be collected. Simple distillation uses a Liebig condenser arranged almost horizontally. When the liquid mixture is heated and vapours are produced, they enter the condenser and then flow away from the flask and can be collected. *Example:* simple distillation of ethanoic acid.

slag: a mixture of substances that are waste products of a furnace. Most slags are composed mainly of silicates.

smelting: roasting a substance in order to extract the metal contained in it.

smog: a mixture of smoke and fog. The term is used to describe city fogs in which there is a large proportion of particulate matter (tiny pieces of carbon from exhausts) and also a high concentration of sulphur and nitrogen gases and probably ozone. *See:* photochemical smog.

smokeless fuel: a fuel which has been subjected to partial pyrolysis, such that there is no more loose particulate matter remaining. *Example:* Coke is a smokeless fuel.

solid/solid phase: a rigid form of matter which maintains its shape, whatever its container.

solubility: the maximum amount of a substance that can be contained in a solvent.

soluble: readily dissolvable in a solvent.

solute: a substance that has dissolved. *Example:* sodium chloride in water.

solution: a mixture of a liquid (the solvent) and at least one other substance of lesser abundance (the solute). Mixtures can be separated by physical means, for example, by evaporation and cooling. *See:* aqueous solution.

solvent: the main substance in a solution.

spectator ions: the ionic part of a compound that does not play an active part in a reaction. *Example:* when magnesium ribbon is placed in copper(II) sulphate solution, the copper is displaced from the solution by the magnesium, while the sulphate ion (SO_4^{2-}) plays no part in the reaction and so behaves as a spectator ion.

spectrum: a progressive series arranged using a characteristic etc. *Examples:* the range of colours that make up visible light (as seen in a rainbow) or across all electromagnetic radiation, arranged in progression according to their wavelength.

spontaneous combustion: the effect of a very reactive material or combination of reactants that suddenly reach their ignition temperature and begin to combust rapidly.

standard temperature and pressure (STP): 0°C at one atmosphere (a pressure which supports a column of mercury 760 mm high). Also given as 0°C at 100 kilopascals. *See:* atmospheric pressure.

state of matter: the physical form of matter. There are three states of matter: liquid, solid and gaseous.

stationary phase: a name given to a material which is used as a medium for separating a liquid mixture in chromatography.

strong acid: an acid that has completely dissociated (ionised) in water. Mineral acids are strong acids.

sublime/sublimation: the change of a substance from solid to gas, or vice versa, without going through a liquid phase. *Example:* iodine sublimes from a purple solid to a purple gas.

substance: a type of material, including mixtures.

sulphate: a compound that includes sulphur and oxygen and contains more oxygen than a sulphite. Sulphate ions have the chemical formula SO_4^{2-}. *Examples:* calcium sulphate $CaSO_4$ (the main

constituent of gypsum) and aluminium sulphate $Al_2(SO_4)_3$ (an alum).

sulphide: a sulphur compound that contains no oxygen. Sulphide ions have the chemical formula S^{2-}. *Example:* hydrogen sulphide (H_2S).

sulphite: a compound that includes sulphur and oxygen but contains less oxygen than a sulphate. Sulphite ions have the chemical formula SO_3^{2-}. *Example:* sodium sulphite Na_2SO_3.

supercooling: the ability of some substances to cool below their normal freezing point. *Example:* sodium thiosulphate.

supersaturated solution: a solution in which the amount of solute is greater than that which would normally be expected in a saturated solution. Most solids are more soluble in hot solutions than in cold. If a hot saturated solution is made up, the solution can be rapidly cooled down below its freezing point before it begins to solidify. This is a supersaturated solution.

surface tension: the force that operates on the surface of a liquid and which makes it act as though it were covered with an invisible, elastic film.

suspension: a mist of tiny particles in a liquid.

synthesis: a reaction in which a substance is formed from simpler reactants. *Example:* hydrogen gas and chlorine gas react to sythesise hydrogen chloride gas. The term can also be applied to polymerisation of organic compounds.

synthetic: does not occur naturally but has to be manufactured. Commonly used in the name 'synthetic fibre'.

tare: an allowance made for the weight of a container.

tarnish: a coating that develops as a result of the reaction between a metal and substances in the air. The most common form of tarnishing is a very thin, transparent oxide coating.

terminal: one of the electrodes of a battery.

test (chemical): a reagent or a procedure used to reveal the presence of another reagent. *Example:* litmus and other indicators are used to test the acidity or alkalinity of a substance.

test tube: A thin, glass tube, closed at one end and used for chemical tests, etc. The composition and thickness of the glass is such that, while it is inert to most chemical reactions, it may not sustain very high temperatures but can usually be heated in a Bunsen flame. *See:* boiling tube.

thermal decomposition: the breakdown of a substance using heat. *See* pyrolysis.

thermoplastic: a plastic that will soften and can be moulded repeatedly into shape on heating and will set into the moulded shape as it cools.

thermoset: a plastic that will set into a moulded shape as it cools, but which cannot be made soft by reheating.

thistle funnel: a narrow tube, expanded at the top into a thistlehead-shaped vessel. It is used as a funnel when introducing small amounts of liquid reactant. When fitted with a tap, it can be used to control the rate of entry of a reactant. *See:* burette.

titration: the analysis of the composition of a substance in a solution by measuring the volume of that solution (the titrant, normally in a burette) needed to react with a given volume of another solution (the titrate, normally placed in a flask). An indicator is often used to signal

change. *Example:* neutralisation of sodium hydroxide using hydrochloric acid in an acid–base titration. *See:* end point.

toxic: poisonous.

transition metals: the group of metals that belong to the d-block of the Periodic Table. Transition metals commonly have a number of differently coloured oxidation states. *Examples:* iron, vanadium.

Universal Indicator: a mixture of indicators commonly used in the laboratory because of its reliability. Used as a solution or impregnated into paper (Indicator paper), which is dampened before use. Universal Indicator changes colour from purple in a strongly alkaline solution through green when the solution is neutral to red in strongly acidic solutions. Universal Indicator is more accurate than litmus paper but less accurate than a pH meter.

unsaturated hydrocarbon: a hydrocarbon, in which at least one bond is a double or triple bond. Hydrogen atoms can be added to unsaturated compounds to form saturated compounds. *Example:* ethene, C_2H_4 or $CH_2=CH_2$.

vacuum: a container from which air has been removed using a pump.

valency: the number of bonds that an atom can form. *Examples:* calcium has a valency of 2 and bromine a valency of 1

valency shell: the outermost shell of an atom. *See:* shell.

vapour: the gaseous phase of a substance that is a liquid or a solid at that temperature. *Examples:* water vapour is the gaseous form of water, iodine vapour is the gaseous form of solid iodine. *See:* gas.

vein: a fissure in rock that has filled with ore or other mineral-bearing rock.

viscous: slow-moving, syrupy. A liquid that has a low viscosity is said to be mobile.

volatile: readily forms a gas.

volatile fraction: the part of a liquid mixture that will vaporise readily under the conditions prevailing during the reaction. *See:* fraction, vapour.

water of crystallisation: the water molecules absorbed into the crystalline structure as a liquid changes to a solid. *Example:* hydrated copper(II) sulphate $CuSO_4 \bullet 5H_2O$. *See:* hydrate.

weak acid and **weak base**: an acid or base that has only partly dissociated (ionised) in water. Most organic acids are weak acids. *See:* organic acid.

weight: the gravitational force on a substance. *See:* mass.

X-rays: a form of very short wave radiation.

MASTER INDEX

78